Are there cars on Mars?

Contributor: Carole Stott

Contents

Quiz number
Each quiz is numbered, so you can look up the relevant set of answers by quiz number.

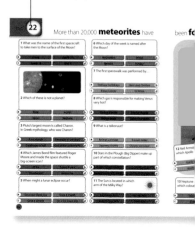

22   More than 20,000 **meteorites** have been fo

1 What was the name of the first spacecraft to take men to the surface of the Moon?

2 Which of these is not a planet?

3 Pluto's largest moon is called Charon. In Greek mythology, who was Charon?

4 Which James Bond film featured Roger Moore and made the space shuttle a big-screen icon?

5 When might a lunar eclipse occur?

6 Which day of the week is named after the Moon?

7 The first spacewalk was performed by...

8 Which gas is responsible for making Venus very hot?

9 What is a taikonaut?

10 Stars in the Plough (Big Dipper) make up part of which constellation?

11 The Sun is located in which arm of the Milky Way?

12 Neil Armstrong which Apollo

13 Neptune which colour

Reference

The Sun and the Solar System
The Sun and the large number of much smaller objects that orbit around it are together known as the Solar System. They have been together for about 4.6 billion years, ever since they formed from a huge, spinning cloud of gas and dust called the solar nebula. The Sun is made of 99.8 per cent of the system's material and its powerful gravity keeps the system together.

The Sun and its family
After the Sun, the largest Solar System objects are the eight planets, which between them have 168 moons. Smaller than the planets are five dwarf planets, billions of asteroids, Kuiper Belt objects, and comets.

Formation of the Solar System
The Solar System started to take shape when gravity pulled the solar nebula's material inwards. The nebula's centre became denser, heated up, and formed the Sun. Unused material bumped and joined and slowly formed the planets.

Centre of solar nebula becomes dense and heats up

A spinning disc of unused material surrounds the young Sun

Disc material joins to form planets

Picture questions
Every quiz has at least two picture questions, testing your visual memory.

14 How many moons does Jupiter have?

27

How to use this book

Each quiz is given a difficulty rating – easy (green), medium (blue), or hard (red) – as well as a quiz number. The questions are also numbered, with multiple-choice answers. Each question is colour-coded, so you know which reference page to turn to if you want to find out more about a particular subject. The answers are laid out in a clear, easy-to-use section at the back of the book.

Learning more
You'll find fun facts on every page.

Most **Kuiper Belt** objects take more than 250 years to **orbit** the Sun ◖ Difficulty level **Hard**

1 Which theory states that the Universe has no beginning and no end?

2 The highest response to a NASA job advert for astronauts was in 1978. How many people applied?

3 Which satellite monitors Earth's polar ice sheets?

4 Which is the largest satellite of the dwarf

7 Comets that come extremely close to the Sun are called…

8 What is the axial tilt of Uranus?

9 The first systematic naming of stars was introduced in 1603. Who introduced it?

Reference

What's in a name?
Solar System objects are named according to guidelines. The planets are named after ancient gods and goddesses. Jupiter takes its name from the king of the Roman gods (left). Comets are named after their discoverers, and asteroids have a wide range of names, including those of astronomers, musicians, and fictional characters such as Pinocchio.

…e shows Apollo 11's lander, …was its landing site?

---

11 How long does the Sun take to rotate on its axis?

12 Which of Saturn's moons has an irregular-shaped, sponge-like appearance?

- Titan
- Hyperion
- Dione
- Iapetus

13 The Deep Impact probe was designed to study the interior of which comet?

14 Extremely luminous stars that have exhausted the hydrogen fuel in their cores are called…

15 How fast must a spacecraft move to escape Earth's gravitational pull?

- 11kps (7mps)
- 17kps (11mps)
- 8kps (5mps)

16 Which is the biggest canyon system in the Solar System?

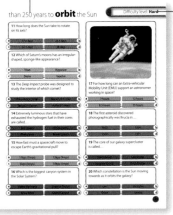

17 For how long can an Extra-vehicular Mobility Unit (EMU) support an astronaut working in space?

- 7 hours
- 12 hours
- 8.5 hours
- 11 hours

18 The first asteroid discovered photographically was Brucia in…

19 The core of our galaxy supercluster is called…

20 Which constellation is the Sun moving towards as it orbits the galaxy?

Difficulty rating
Choose between easy, medium, and hard quizzes, depending on how bright you're feeling. The level of each quiz is clearly indicated.

Solar surface
…ent, active place. Its visible …ere, consists of 1,000km- …hot rising gas. Dark spots …n the upward flow of hot …unspots typically last for …often bigger than Earth.

…li million miles) …enough for our …in our sky. Its …0°C (9,900°F) …our. It provides …use it to

Sun's energy
Energy produced by nuclear reactions in the Sun's core is released through its surface. Short-lived jets of gas leap up constantly. Bursts of energy called flares also explode out of the surface. Giant clouds of gas that loop and arch into space are prominences that can last for months.

Reference colour
Match the colour of the question to the colour of the reference page tab, and find out more about the subjects that interest you.

Our galaxy, the **Milky Way**,

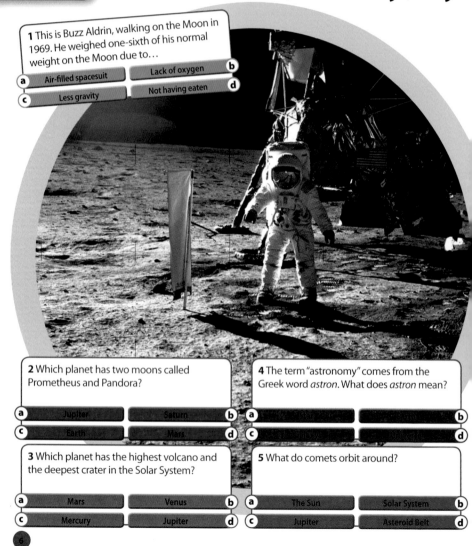

1 This is Buzz Aldrin, walking on the Moon in 1969. He weighed one-sixth of his normal weight on the Moon due to…

- **a** Air-filled spacesuit
- **b** Lack of oxygen
- **c** Less gravity
- **d** Not having eaten

2 Which planet has two moons called Prometheus and Pandora?

- **a** Jupiter
- **b** Saturn
- **c** Earth
- **d** Mars

3 Which planet has the highest volcano and the deepest crater in the Solar System?

- **a** Mars
- **b** Venus
- **c** Mercury
- **d** Jupiter

4 The term "astronomy" comes from the Greek word *astron*. What does *astron* mean?

- **a**
- **b**
- **c**
- **d**

5 What do comets orbit around?

- **a** The Sun
- **b** Solar System
- **c** Jupiter
- **d** Asteroid Belt

has about 400 billion **stars**

6 Which spacecraft discovered the Tsiolkovsky Crater on the Moon?

- **a** Apollo 16
- **b** Apollo 17
- **c** Luna 3
- **d** Apollo 11

7 Which is the largest constellation?

- **a** Draco
- **b** Orion
- **c** Aquila
- **d** Hydra

8 Which of these is not a Kuiper Belt object?

- **a** Pluto
- **b** Sedna
- **c** Haumea
- **d** Miranda

9 How wide is the Milky Way Galaxy?

- **a** 200,000 light years
- **b** 100,000 light years
- **c** 50,000 light years
- **d** 150,000 light years

10 Which planet in the Solar System is the least dense?

- **a** Neptune
- **b** Jupiter
- **c** Saturn
- **d** Mercury

11 Who was the first person to go into space?

- **a** Yuri Gagarin
- **b** Alan Shepard
- **c** Neil Armstrong
- **d** Buzz Aldrin

12 Where would you find Mare Tranquillitatis?

- **a** Mercury
- **b** The Moon
- **c** Mars
- **d** Miranda

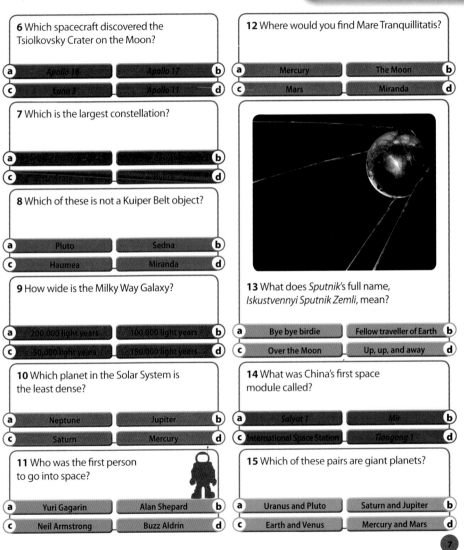

13 What does *Sputnik*'s full name, *Iskustvennyi Sputnik Zemli*, mean?

- **a** Bye bye birdie
- **b** Fellow traveller of Earth
- **c** Over the Moon
- **d** Up, up, and away

14 What was China's first space module called?

- **a** Salyut 1
- **b** Mir
- **c** International Space Station
- **d** Tiangong 1

15 Which of these pairs are giant planets?

- **a** Uranus and Pluto
- **b** Saturn and Jupiter
- **c** Earth and Venus
- **d** Mercury and Mars

The Universe started with a **Big Bang**

1 Charged particles ejected from the upper atmosphere of the Sun are called…

a Radiation
b Solar wind
c Sunspots
d Solar flares

2 What are the brightest objects in the Universe called?

a Stars
b Galaxies
c Planets
d Quasars

3 Which is the oldest type of star?

a
b
c
d

4 How would the Moon appear in the first quarter of its lunar phase?

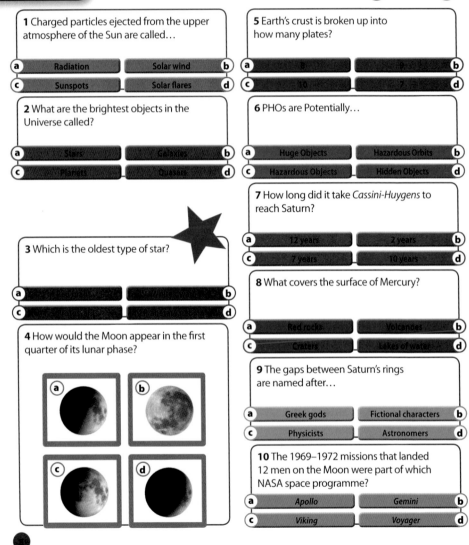

a
b
c
d

5 Earth's crust is broken up into how many plates?

a 8
b 9
c 10
d 7

6 PHOs are Potentially…

a Huge Objects
b Hazardous Orbits
c Hazardous Objects
d Hidden Objects

7 How long did it take *Cassini-Huygens* to reach Saturn?

a 12 years
b 2 years
c 7 years
d 10 years

8 What covers the surface of Mercury?

a Red rocks
b Volcanoes
c Craters
d Lakes of water

9 The gaps between Saturn's rings are named after…

a Greek gods
b Fictional characters
c Physicists
d Astronomers

10 The 1969–1972 missions that landed 12 men on the Moon were part of which NASA space programme?

a *Apollo*
b *Gemini*
c *Viking*
d *Voyager*

Difficulty level: **Medium**

11 How many of Jupiter's 63 moons have been discovered since 2000?

a 10
b 35
c 25
d 45

12 Where does Frank Sinatra want to fly to in his classic song?

a Jupiter
b Mars
c Venus
d The Moon

13 Stellar kinematics is the study of the movement of…

a
b Planets
c Moons
d Comets

14 How many meteorite samples have been recovered from Antarctica?

a More than 15,000
b More than 20,000
c More than 8,000
d More than 5,000

15 What is the shape of the Large Magellanic Cloud?

a Elliptical
b Spherical
c Irregular
d Spiral

16 Which composer wrote a piece of "space music" after meeting William Herschel, the discoverer of Uranus?

a Elton John
b Franz Joseph Haydn
c Don Partridge
d David Bowie

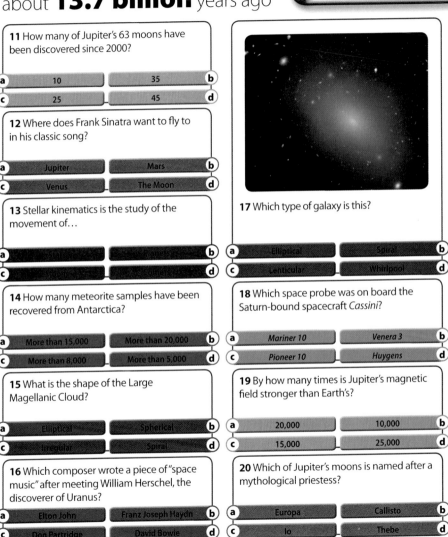

17 Which type of galaxy is this?

a Elliptical
b Spiral
c Lenticular
d Whirlpool

18 Which space probe was on board the Saturn-bound spacecraft *Cassini*?

a Mariner 10
b Venera 3
c Pioneer 10
d Huygens

19 By how many times is Jupiter's magnetic field stronger than Earth's?

a 20,000
b 10,000
c 15,000
d 25,000

20 Which of Jupiter's moons is named after a mythological priestess?

a Europa
b Callisto
c Io
d Thebe

Planets, stars, and **galaxies** make up

1 When Mercury or Venus appear to move across the face of the Sun, what is happening?

a. Eclipse
b. Occulation
c. Obscuration
d. Transit

2 Two of the stars in Ursa Major form a double star. What are their names?

a.
b.
c.
d.

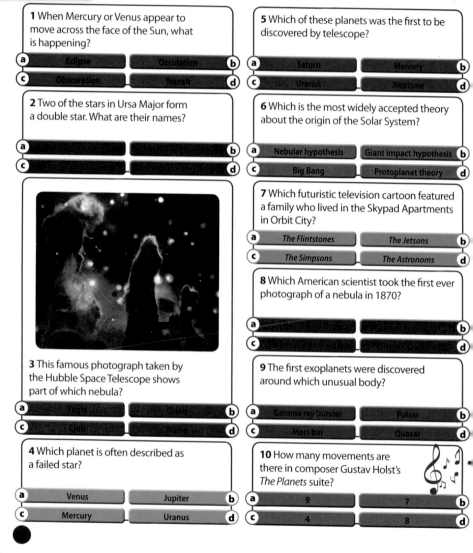

3 This famous photograph taken by the Hubble Space Telescope shows part of which nebula?

a. Eagle
b. Orion
c. Crab
d. Flame

4 Which planet is often described as a failed star?

a. Venus
b. Jupiter
c. Mercury
d. Uranus

5 Which of these planets was the first to be discovered by telescope?

a. Saturn
b. Mercury
c. Uranus
d. Neptune

6 Which is the most widely accepted theory about the origin of the Solar System?

a. Nebular hypothesis
b. Giant impact hypothesis
c. Big Bang
d. Protoplanet theory

7 Which futuristic television cartoon featured a family who lived in the Skypad Apartments in Orbit City?

a. The Flintstones
b. The Jetsons
c. The Simpsons
d. The Astronoms

8 Which American scientist took the first ever photograph of a nebula in 1870?

a.
b.
c.
d.

9 The first exoplanets were discovered around which unusual body?

a. Gamma ray burster
b. Pulsar
c. Mars bar
d. Quasar

10 How many movements are there in composer Gustav Holst's *The Planets* suite?

a. 9
b. 7
c. 4
d. 8

less than 5 per cent of the Universe

11 Who discovered that the Universe is expanding?

a Alan Guth
b Edwin Hubble
c George Lemaître
d George Gamow

12 Nebulae that produce a brilliant glow are called…

a Planetaries
b Absorption
c Emission
d Bright

13 How many Kuiper Belt objects have been identified so far?

a More than 5,000
b Less than 1,000
c More than 1,300
d About 3,000

14 Only one part of the *Apollo 11* lunar mission returned to Earth. Which part was it?

a Command module
b Service module
c Lunar module
d Solid fuel boosters

15 A galaxy within which stars form at an exceptionally rapid rate is known as a…

a Spinning galaxy
b Foetal galaxy
c Seeded galaxy
d Starburst

16 In *The Hitchhiker's Guide to the Galaxy*, members of which alien race plan to destroy Earth?

a The Beeblebrox
b The Dents
c The Mice
d The Vogons

17 Which scientist worked on the idea of a laser-driven spacecraft?

a Henry Draper
b Daniel Kirkwood
c Edward Barnard
d Robert Forward

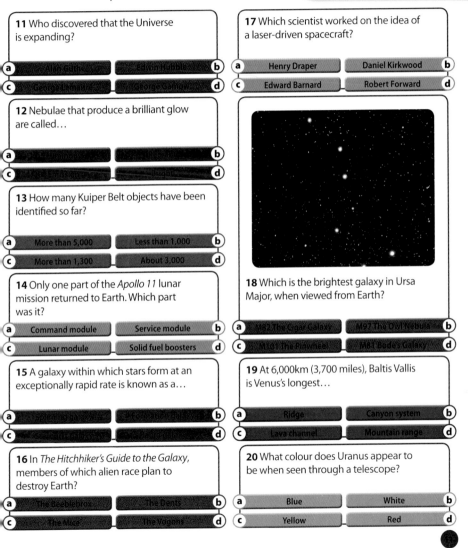

18 Which is the brightest galaxy in Ursa Major, when viewed from Earth?

a M82 The Cigar Galaxy
b M97 The Owl Nebula
c M101 The Pinwheel
d M81 Bode's Galaxy

19 At 6,000km (3,700 miles), Baltis Vallis is Venus's longest…

a Ridge
b Canyon system
c Lava channel
d Mountain range

20 What colour does Uranus appear to be when seen through a telescope?

a Blue
b White
c Yellow
d Red

There are at least **125 billion**

1 What does this chart show?

(a)

(b)

(c)

(d)

3 Which of the following planets has no moon?

(a) Mars

(b) Neptune

(c) Earth

(d) Venus

2 "To infinity and beyond!" is the popular catch phrase of which animated character?

(a) Captain Caveman

(b) Buzz Lightyear

(c) Space Ghost

(d) Superman

4 Which is the smallest dwarf planet?

(a) Haumea

(b) Eris

(c) Pluto

(d) Ceres

galaxies in the **Universe**

Difficulty level: **Easy**

5 Science-fiction writer Arthur C Clarke examined the problems of colonizing worlds like Mars in his book…

- **a** Red Planet
- **b** The Sands of Mars
- **c** Martians
- **d** Mars Attacks!

6 Which celestial body does the International Space Station orbit?

- **a** Milky Way
- **b** It is stationary
- **c** Earth
- **d** The Sun

7 Which planet is named after the Roman goddess of love?

- **a** Venus
- **b** Uranus
- **c** Saturn
- **d** Mars

8 Which constellation is represented by The Twins?

- **a** Taurus
- **b** Aquarius
- **c** Gemini
- **d** Cancer

9 What was Superman's home planet called?

- **a** Krypton
- **b** Mogo
- **c** Korugar
- **d** Tamaran

10 On average, how often does a solar eclipse occur?

- **a** Every 18 months
- **b** Every month
- **c** Every 3 years
- **d** Every 5 years

11 Which planet spins round once in the shortest time of 9.9 hours?

- **a** Jupiter
- **b** Saturn
- **c** Uranus
- **d** Mercury

12 Manned or unmanned travel between stars is called…

- **a** Intergalactic travel
- **b** Orbital travel
- **c** Interstellar travel
- **d** Interspace travel

13 Which planet is sometimes called the Evening Star?

- **a** Mercury
- **b** Venus
- **c** Uranus
- **d** Jupiter

14 In 2003 which space shuttle burst into flames upon re-entering Earth's atmosphere, killing all seven astronauts on board?

- **a** Enterprise
- **b** Atlantis
- **c** Challenger
- **d** Columbia

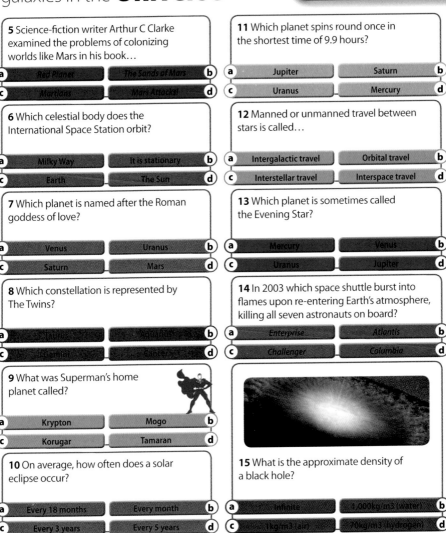

15 What is the approximate density of a black hole?

- **a** Infinite
- **b** 1,000kg/m3 (water)
- **c** 1kg/m3 (air)
- **d** 70kg/m3 (hydrogen)

13

1 A star that appears to change in brightness is called a...

a
b
c
d

2 According to the Hubble Space Telescope's 1999 estimate, how many galaxies are there in the Universe?

a 125 billion
b 125 million
c 10 billion
d 10 million

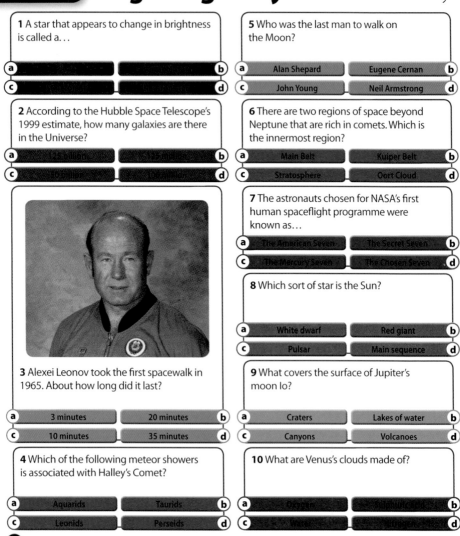

3 Alexei Leonov took the first spacewalk in 1965. About how long did it last?

a 3 minutes
b 20 minutes
c 10 minutes
d 35 minutes

4 Which of the following meteor showers is associated with Halley's Comet?

a Aquarids
b Taurids
c Leonids
d Perseids

5 Who was the last man to walk on the Moon?

a Alan Shepard
b Eugene Cernan
c John Young
d Neil Armstrong

6 There are two regions of space beyond Neptune that are rich in comets. Which is the innermost region?

a Main Belt
b Kuiper Belt
c Stratosphere
d Oort Cloud

7 The astronauts chosen for NASA's first human spaceflight programme were known as...

a The American Seven
b The Secret Seven
c The Mercury Seven
d The Chosen Seven

8 Which sort of star is the Sun?

a White dwarf
b Red giant
c Pulsar
d Main sequence

9 What covers the surface of Jupiter's moon Io?

a Craters
b Lakes of water
c Canyons
d Volcanoes

10 What are Venus's clouds made of?

a Oxygen
b Sulphuric acid
c Water
d Nitrogen

11 The constellation Gemini depicts which mythological twins?

a [blacked out] b [blacked out]
c [blacked out] d [blacked out]

12 Which of the following is not a pair of superior planets?

a Mars and Neptune b Neptune and Uranus
c Mercury and Venus d Jupiter and Saturn

13 Which planet has the most eccentric (least circular) and highly inclined orbit in the Solar System?

a Mercury b Mars
c Earth d Jupiter

14 Which animal was aboard the American spaceflight *Little Joe 2*?

15 What is the name of the planet closest to the Sun?

a Mercury b Mars
c Venus d Moon

16 The lunar module of *Apollo 11* was also known as. . .

a Eagle b Lander
c Sparrow d Alien

17 Which of these spacecraft orbited Venus?

a Cassini b Viking
c Magellan d Apollo

18 A meteorite fell in Australia in 1969. What is its name?

a Mundrabilla b Mumpeowie
c Molong d Murchison

19 Which of the following is not a dwarf planet?

a Pluto b Haumea
c Eris d Eros

20 Who made the first detailed observation of Jupiter?

a Johannes Kepler b Giovanni Cassini
c Galileo Galilei d Tycho Brahe

Saturn has the **lowest**

1 The two-piece spacesuits worn by astronauts during spacewalks are called extra-vehicular…

a Mobility units

b Spacewalk support

c Mobility gear

d Zero-gravity garments

2 Which planet is sometimes referred to as the Morning Star?

a Saturn

b Venus

c Mars

d Jupiter

3 The stars Merak and Dubhe in Ursa Major point towards which other important star?

a

b

c

d

4 What is the name of this triple system of stars in Earth's neighbourhood?

a Alpha Centauri

b Cygni

c Sirius

d Procyon

5 All Venusian features are named after women, except this one. What is its name?

a Copernicus Crater

b Maxwell Montes

c Olympus Mons

d Pike's Peak

6 Who first described the "canals" on Mars?

a Nicholas Copernicus

b Edmond Halley

c Giovanni Schiaparelli

d Johannes Kepler

7 "I don't think the human race will survive the next thousand years, unless we spread into space." Who said this?

a Brian Cox

b Stephen Hawking

c Carl Sagan

d H G Wells

8 What did the Universe essentially consist of just a second after its birth?

a Neutrons

b Electrons

c Photons

d

9 What are "sporadics"?

a Partial eclipses

b Solar flares

c Volcanoes on Venus

d Non-shower meteors

10 Which of Saturn's moons has a bright, icy face on one half, and a dark, less reflective face on the other?

a Iapetus

b Phoebe

c Prometheus

d Albiorix

density of all the planets

11 Where would you find a white, oval storm?

a Jupiter
b Venus
c Mercury
d Titan

12 Which animal does the constellation Camelopardalis represent?

a Camel
b
c Horse
d Giraffe

13 What are the units for right ascension?

a Metres
b Joules
c Hours
d Degrees

14 Which impact crater, located on Mars, is the largest in the Solar System?

a Hellas Basin
b Isidis Planitia
c Huygens
d North Polar Basin

15 In which year did the US spacecraft *Mars Pathfinder* land on planet Mars?

a 1996
b 1998
c 1999
d 1997

16 How many astronomical units away from the Sun is the Oort Cloud?

a 75,000
b 83,000
c 50,000
d 100,000

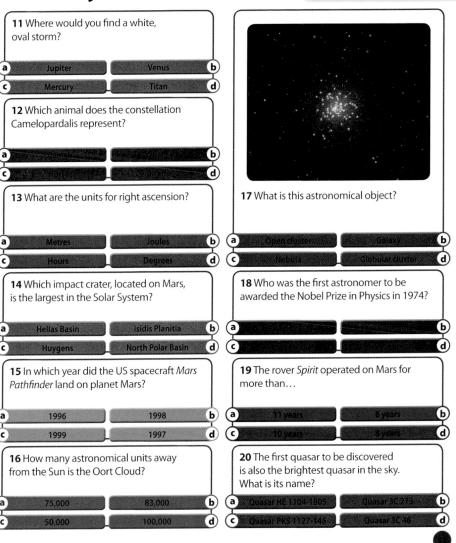

17 What is this astronomical object?

a Open cluster
b Galaxy
c Nebula
d Globular cluster

18 Who was the first astronomer to be awarded the Nobel Prize in Physics in 1974?

a
b
c
d

19 The rover *Spirit* operated on Mars for more than…

a 11 years
b 6 years
c 10 years
d 8 years

20 The first quasar to be discovered is also the brightest quasar in the sky. What is its name?

a Quasar HE 1104-1805
b Quasar 3C 273
c Quasar PKS 1127-145
d Quasar 3C 48

Earth is the **only** place in the

1 Which 1968 film is thought of as a scientifically accurate portrayal of life and travel in space?

- (a) Mars Attacks!
- (b) 2001: A Space Odyssey
- (c) Apollo 13
- (d) Battle Beyond the Stars

2 How long does Mercury take to rotate once on its axis?

- (a) 89.2 days
- (b) 58.6 days
- (c) 20 days
- (d) 44 days

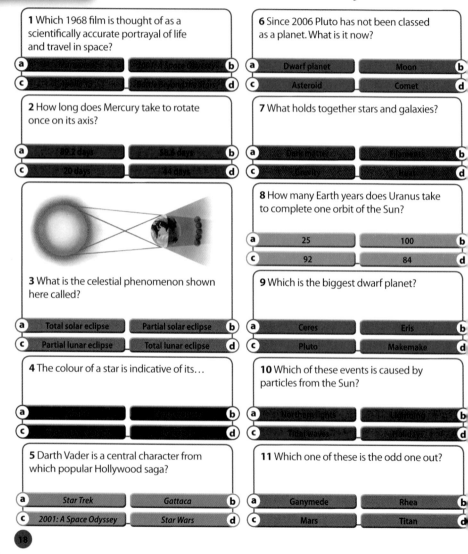

3 What is the celestial phenomenon shown here called?

- (a) Total solar eclipse
- (b) Partial solar eclipse
- (c) Partial lunar eclipse
- (d) Total lunar eclipse

4 The colour of a star is indicative of its…

- (a)
- (b)
- (c)
- (d)

5 Darth Vader is a central character from which popular Hollywood saga?

- (a) Star Trek
- (b) Gattaca
- (c) 2001: A Space Odyssey
- (d) Star Wars

6 Since 2006 Pluto has not been classed as a planet. What is it now?

- (a) Dwarf planet
- (b) Moon
- (c) Asteroid
- (d) Comet

7 What holds together stars and galaxies?

- (a) Dark matter
- (b) Filaments
- (c) Gravity
- (d) Heat

8 How many Earth years does Uranus take to complete one orbit of the Sun?

- (a) 25
- (b) 100
- (c) 92
- (d) 84

9 Which is the biggest dwarf planet?

- (a) Ceres
- (b) Eris
- (c) Pluto
- (d) Makemake

10 Which of these events is caused by particles from the Sun?

- (a) Northern lights
- (b) Lightning
- (c) Tidal waves
- (d) Holidays

11 Which one of these is the odd one out?

- (a) Ganymede
- (b) Rhea
- (c) Mars
- (d) Titan

Universe known to have **life**

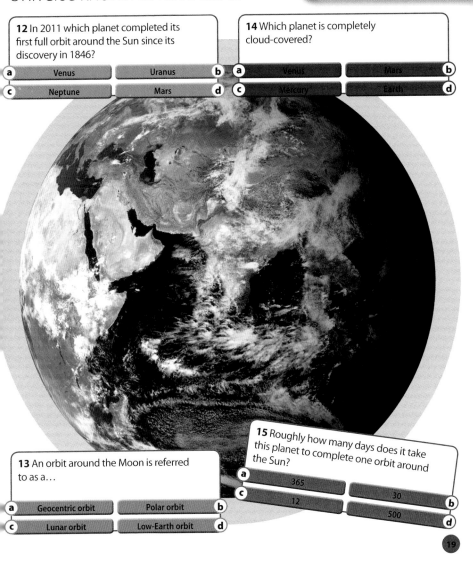

12 In 2011 which planet completed its first full orbit around the Sun since its discovery in 1846?

a Venus   Uranus **b**

c Neptune   Mars **d**

14 Which planet is completely cloud-covered?

a Venus   Mars **b**

c Mercury   Earth **d**

15 Roughly how many days does it take this planet to complete one orbit around the Sun?

a 365

c 12   30 **b**

   500 **d**

13 An orbit around the Moon is referred to as a…

a Geocentric orbit   Polar orbit **b**

c Lunar orbit   Low-Earth orbit **d**

1 Which objects make up the Oort Cloud?

a Moons
b Stars
c Comets
d Asteroids

2 The journey of *Voyager 2* to the four giant planets is known as the…

a Great Voyage
b Great Expedition
c Grand Excursion
d Grand Tour

3 Which was the first planet, other than Earth, to be fully orbited by a spacecraft?

a Mars
b Venus
c Saturn
d Mercury

4 Which spacecraft discovered Jupiter's rings?

a *Voyager 1*
b *Voyager 2*
c *Messenger*
d *Cassini*

5 Nine manned missions have travelled as far as the Moon, but how many have landed on it?

a 4
b 8
c 6
d 9

6 The Leonid meteor shower is associated with which comet?

a Hale–Bopp
b Tempel–Tuttle
c Halley
d Encke

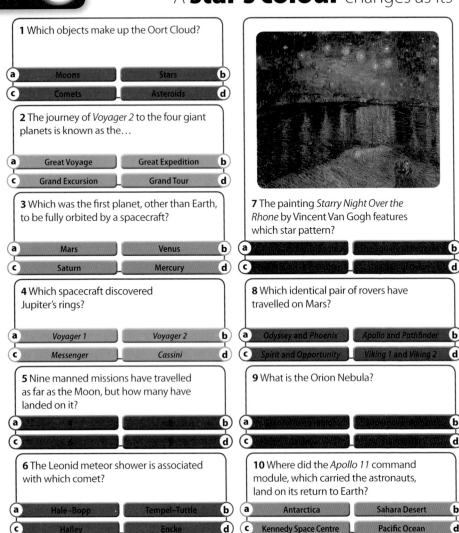

7 The painting *Starry Night Over the Rhone* by Vincent Van Gogh features which star pattern?

a
b
c
d

8 Which identical pair of rovers have travelled on Mars?

a *Odyssey* and *Phoenix*
b *Apollo* and *Pathfinder*
c *Spirit* and *Opportunity*
d *Viking 1* and *Viking 2*

9 What is the Orion Nebula?

a
b
c
d

10 Where did the *Apollo 11* command module, which carried the astronauts, land on its return to Earth?

a Antarctica
b Sahara Desert
c Kennedy Space Centre
d Pacific Ocean

temperature changes

11 Which liquid is present on the surface of Saturn's moon Titan?

a) Acetic acid
b) Liquid hydrogen
c) Methane
d) Sulphuric acid

12 Who became the world's first space tourist in 2001 and travelled in space for eight days?

a) Gregory Olsen
b) Dennis Tito
c) Carl Walz
d) John Young

13 The Kármán line is an imaginary boundary between Earth's atmosphere and outer space. How far is it from sea level?

a) 100km (62 miles)
b) 1,500km (932 miles)
c) 500km (311 miles)
d) 1,000km (621 miles)

14 Which of Saturn's moons did the *Huygens* probe visit?

a) Mimas
b) Titan
c) Dione
d) Tethys

15 Which planet in the Solar System is most similar to Earth?

a) Mars
b) Mercury
c) Jupiter
d) Venus

16 Stars of which colour are the hottest?

a) White
b) Yellow
c) Blue
d) Red

17 In Greek mythology, who was Uranus?

a) God of love
b) God of heavens
c) God of war
d) God of power

18 The Large and Small Magellanic Clouds are named after a Portuguese explorer. What was his name?

a) Fabio Magellan
b) Francisco Magellan
c) Piotro Magellan
d) Ferdinand Magellan

19 What is the asterism from the constellation Cygnus called?

a)
b)
c)
d)

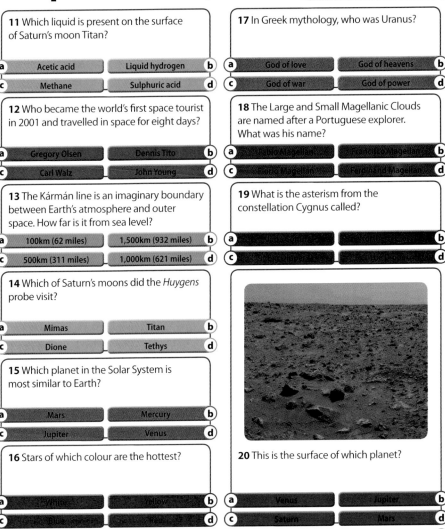

20 This is the surface of which planet?

a) Venus
b) Jupiter
c) Saturn
d) Mars

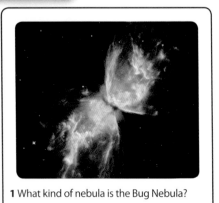

1 What kind of nebula is the Bug Nebula?

a
b
c
d

2 UGC 10214 is a distorted galaxy 420 million light years away. What is its nickname?

a Tadpole | b Horsehead
c Pinwheel | d Crab

3 What do astronomers call the small particles of rocky debris orbiting the Sun in interplanetary space?

a Meteorites | b Meteors
c Meteorines | d Meteoroids

4 The spectacular Herschel Crater covers a large part of the surface of which of Saturn's moons?

a Skathi | b Mimas
c Tarvos | d Epimetheus

5 What is Pleiades (M45) a type of?

a Globular cluster | b Galaxy
c Nebula | d Open cluster

6 Where was *Vostok 1*, the first manned spacecraft, launched from in 1961?

a Uchinoura Space Centre | b Baikonur Cosmodrome
c Cape Canaveral | d Guiana Space Centre

7 How far above Earth does space start?

a 150km (93 miles) | b 200km (124 miles)
c 250km (155 miles) | d 100km (62 miles)

8 Which of these objects is the brightest when viewed from Earth? (*m* = apparent magnitude)

a Saturn (*m* = -0.3) | b Pluto (*m* = 13.8)
c The Sun (*m* = -26.7) | d Mars (*m* = -2.9)

9 How much memory did the lunar module computer on *Apollo 11* have?

a 71 kilobytes | b 700 kilobytes
c 100 kilobytes | d 84 kilobytes

10 Which planets are known as the "inferior" planets?

a Neptune and Pluto | b Mercury and Venus
c Jupiter and Saturn | d Uranus and Neptune

11 Which instrument was set up on the surface of the Moon during the 1969 *Apollo 11* mission?

a Astroscope

b Coronagraph

c Spherograph

d Seismometer

12 Which planets are known as the "ice giants"?

a Uranus and Neptune

b Earth and Mars

c Jupiter and Saturn

d Mercury and Venus

13 The Hubble Telescope discovered the smallest-known Kuiper Belt object in…

a 2008

b 2010

c 2009

d 2005

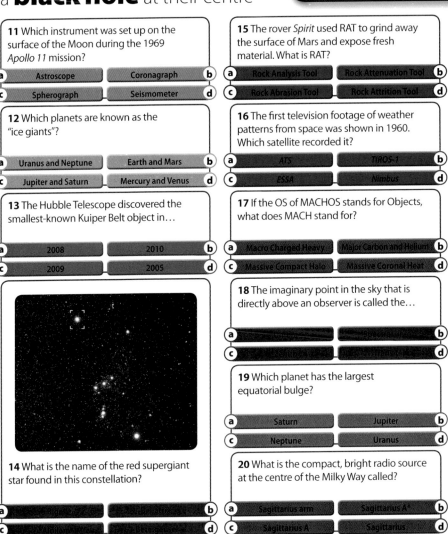

14 What is the name of the red supergiant star found in this constellation?

a Rigel

b Bellatrix

c Alnilam

d Betelgeuse

15 The rover *Spirit* used RAT to grind away the surface of Mars and expose fresh material. What is RAT?

a Rock Analysis Tool

b Rock Attenuation Tool

c Rock Abrasion Tool

d Rock Attrition Tool

16 The first television footage of weather patterns from space was shown in 1960. Which satellite recorded it?

a ATS

b TIROS-1

c ESSA

d Nimbus

17 If the OS of MACHOS stands for Objects, what does MACH stand for?

a Macro Charged Heavy

b Major Carbon and Helium

c Massive Compact Halo

d Massive Coronal Heat

18 The imaginary point in the sky that is directly above an observer is called the…

a

b

c

d

19 Which planet has the largest equatorial bulge?

a Saturn

b Jupiter

c Neptune

d Uranus

20 What is the compact, bright radio source at the centre of the Milky Way called?

a Sagittarius arm

b Sagittarius A*

c Sagittarius A

d Sagittarius

Jupiter and **Saturn** each

1 The Italian Renaissance painter Sandro Botticelli painted the famous *Birth of…*

a Venus
b Mars
c Earth
d Mercury

2 Which galaxy orbits the Milky Way Galaxy?

a Large Magellanic Cloud
b Sombrero
c Pinwheel
d Centaurus A

3 The study of the chemical composition and temperature of stars is called…

a
b
c
d

4 Roughly 23 per cent of the Universe is made up of this invisible matter. What is it called?

a White matter
b Black matter
c Grey matter
d Dark matter

5 When was the first exoplanet found?

a 1985
b 1992
c 1990
d 2000

6 How long does it take sunlight to reach Earth?

a 6 minutes, 18 seconds
b 9 minutes, 18 seconds
c 8 minutes, 18 seconds
d 7 minutes, 18 seconds

7 This machine recreates the conditions of a spaceflight and helps astronauts train for missions. What is it called?

a Simulator
b Orbiter
c Fairing
d Dock

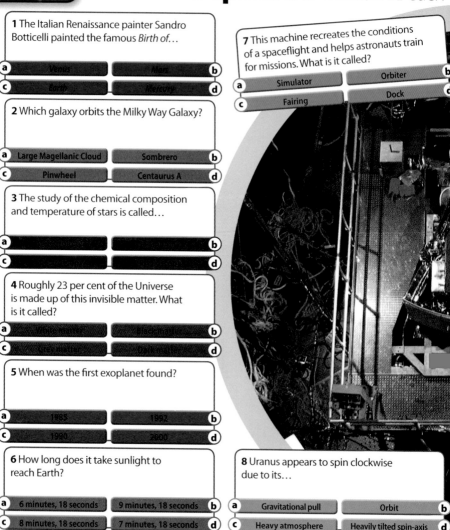

8 Uranus appears to spin clockwise due to its…

a Gravitational pull
b Orbit
c Heavy atmosphere
d Heavily tilted spin-axis

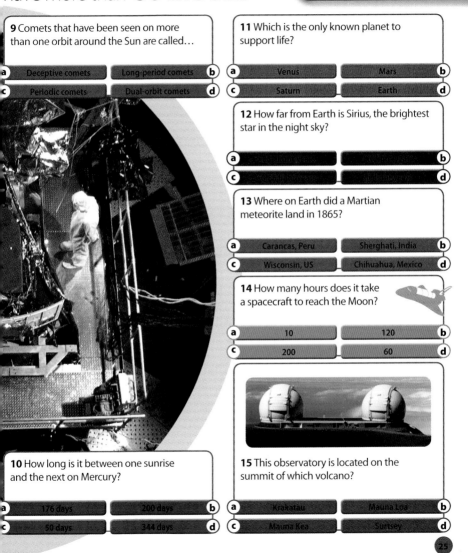

9 Comets that have been seen on more than one orbit around the Sun are called…

a Deceptive comets
b Long-period comets
c Periodic comets
d Dual-orbit comets

10 How long is it between one sunrise and the next on Mercury?

a 176 days
b 200 days
c 50 days
d 344 days

11 Which is the only known planet to support life?

a Venus
b Mars
c Saturn
d Earth

12 How far from Earth is Sirius, the brightest star in the night sky?

a
b
c
d

13 Where on Earth did a Martian meteorite land in 1865?

a Carancas, Peru
b Sherghati, India
c Wisconsin, US
d Chihuahua, Mexico

14 How many hours does it take a spacecraft to reach the Moon?

a 10
b 120
c 200
d 60

15 This observatory is located on the summit of which volcano?

a Krakatau
b Mauna Loa
c Mauna Kea
d Surtsey

1 Which planet's composition is similar to that of a star?

a Uranus
b Jupiter
c Mercury
d Venus

2 Which winds cause dark trails on the surface of Mars?

a Contrails
b Dust whirls
c Tornadoes
d Dust devils

3 What did William Herschel discover in March 1781?

a Pluto
b That planets orbit the Sun
c Uranus
d Neptune

4 Itokawa is an irregular-shaped asteroid made of silicate rock. Which country sent a craft to observe it?

a Japan
b US
c India
d China

5 Which spacecraft has travelled the furthest from Earth?

a Voyager 1
b Mariner 10
c Cassini
d Luna 3

6 How much Moon rock has been brought back to Earth?

a 582kg (1,284lb)
b 882kg (1,945lb)
c 382kg (843lb)
d 182kg (402lb)

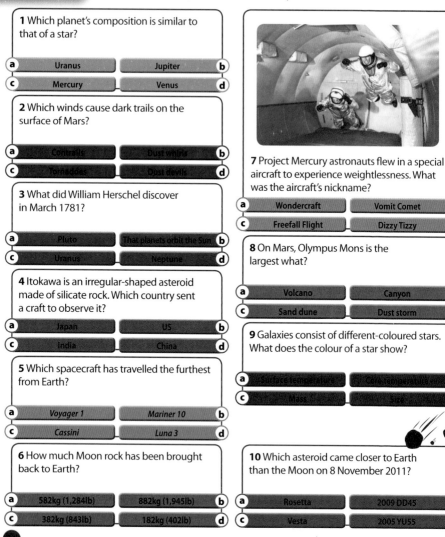

7 Project Mercury astronauts flew in a special aircraft to experience weightlessness. What was the aircraft's nickname?

a Wondercraft
b Vomit Comet
c Freefall Flight
d Dizzy Tizzy

8 On Mars, Olympus Mons is the largest what?

a Volcano
b Canyon
c Sand dune
d Dust storm

9 Galaxies consist of different-coloured stars. What does the colour of a star show?

a Surface temperature
b Core temperature
c Mass
d Size

10 Which asteroid came closer to Earth than the Moon on 8 November 2011?

a Rosetta
b 2009 DD45
c Vesta
d 2005 YU55

Venus is **longer** than its year

11 In Roman mythology, who was Saturn?

a God of war
b God of strength
c God of agriculture
d God of fertility

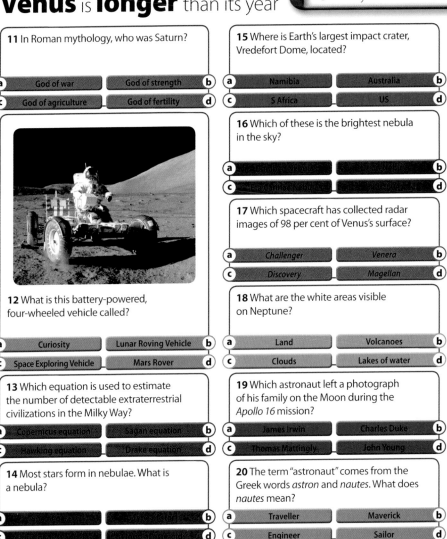

12 What is this battery-powered, four-wheeled vehicle called?

a Curiosity
b Lunar Roving Vehicle
c Space Exploring Vehicle
d Mars Rover

13 Which equation is used to estimate the number of detectable extraterrestrial civilizations in the Milky Way?

a Copernicus equation
b Sagan equation
c Hawking equation
d Drake equation

14 Most stars form in nebulae. What is a nebula?

a
b
c
d

15 Where is Earth's largest impact crater, Vredefort Dome, located?

a Namibia
b Australia
c S Africa
d US

16 Which of these is the brightest nebula in the sky?

a
b
c
d

17 Which spacecraft has collected radar images of 98 per cent of Venus's surface?

a Challenger
b Venera
c Discovery
d Magellan

18 What are the white areas visible on Neptune?

a Land
b Volcanoes
c Clouds
d Lakes of water

19 Which astronaut left a photograph of his family on the Moon during the *Apollo 16* mission?

a James Irwin
b Charles Duke
c Thomas Mattingly
d John Young

20 The term "astronaut" comes from the Greek words *astron* and *nautes*. What does *nautes* mean?

a Traveller
b Maverick
c Engineer
d Sailor

1 All of the planets are visible to the naked eye apart from one. Which one?

- **a** Saturn
- **b** Neptune
- **c** Mercury
- **d** Uranus

2 What is the brightest object in the Kuiper Belt?

- **a** Eris
- **b** Sedna
- **c** Dysnomia
- **d** Pluto

3 When did NASA's Space Shuttle first take to the air?

- **a** 1989
- **b** 1981
- **c** 1985
- **d** 1977

4 Which physicist first developed the idea of cosmic inflation?

- **a** Toshihide Maskawa
- **b** Alan Guth
- **c** Pierre-Gilles de Gennes
- **d** Melvin Schwartz

5 Which of these objects cannot be viewed with the naked eye? (*m* = apparent magnitude)

- **a** Mars (*m* = −2.9)
- **b** Saturn (*m* = −0.3)
- **c** Pluto (*m* = 13.8)
- **d** The Sun (*m* = −26.7)

6 When was China's first space module, *Tiangong 1*, launched?

- **a** 2011
- **b** 2010
- **c** 1999
- **d** 1998

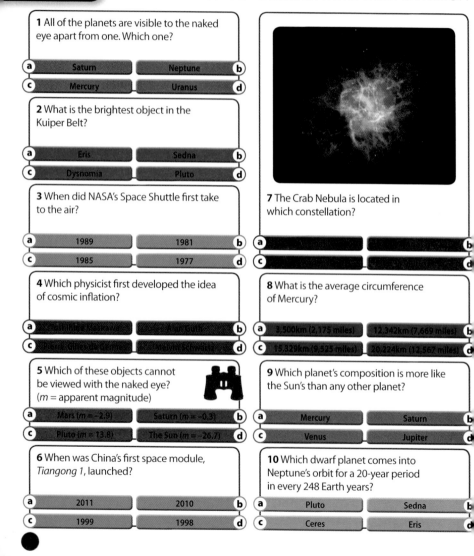

7 The Crab Nebula is located in which constellation?

- **a**
- **b**
- **c**
- **d**

8 What is the average circumference of Mercury?

- **a** 3,500km (2,175 miles)
- **b** 12,342km (7,669 miles)
- **c** 15,329km (9,525 miles)
- **d** 20,224km (12,567 miles)

9 Which planet's composition is more like the Sun's than any other planet?

- **a** Mercury
- **b** Saturn
- **c** Venus
- **d** Jupiter

10 Which dwarf planet comes into Neptune's orbit for a 20-year period in every 248 Earth years?

- **a** Pluto
- **b** Sedna
- **c** Ceres
- **d** Eris

11 Mars's moons Phobos and Deimos were photographed together for the first time in 2009 by which orbiter?

a) Phoenix
b) Mars Express
c) Mars Odyssey
d) Mars Reconnaissance

12 Which of these is the largest trans-Neptunian object?

a) Haumea
b) Makemake
c) Eris
d) Pluto

13 Which very high-mass particle is thought to have existed during the Big Bang and later formed into matter?

a) Quark
b) Positron
c) Electron
d) X-boson

14 Liberty, Equality, and Fraternity are associated with the planet Uranus. What are they?

a) Mountains
b) Arcs of its rings
c) Moons
d) Its rings

15 A person trained to command, pilot, or serve as a crew member on a spacecraft is known as an…

a) Astronomer
b) Astrophysicist
c) Astrobiologist
d) Astronaut

16 M31 and NGC 224 are other names of which galaxy?

a) Ursa Minor
b) Triangulum
c) Andromeda
d) Milky Way

17 What is the name of the blue supergiant star in the constellation of Orion?

a)
b)
c)
d)

18 Who invented the term Big Bang?

a) Fred Hoyle
b) Edwin Hubble
c) Albert Einstein
d) Carl Sagan

19 A group of four identical probes orbit Earth in formation to study its magnetosphere. What are they collectively called?

a) Ulysses
b) Cluster II
c) PROBA-2
d) Euclid

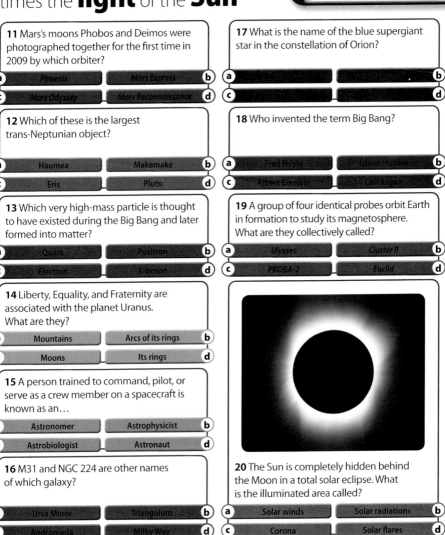

20 The Sun is completely hidden behind the Moon in a total solar eclipse. What is the illuminated area called?

a) Solar winds
b) Solar radiations
c) Corona
d) Solar flares

There are more than **160 moons**

1 What does the constellation Microscopium represent?

a ▮▮▮▮▮▮▮▮▮▮   ▮▮▮▮▮▮▮▮▮▮ b
c ▮▮▮▮▮▮▮▮▮▮   ▮▮▮▮▮▮▮▮▮▮ d

4 What do the planets orbit around?

a Earth   The Sun b
c The Moon   Stars d

2 What was the first animal to orbit Earth?

a Minnie, a cat   Laika, a dog b
c Mickey, a mouse   Chucky, a hen d

5 What are meteors sometimes called?

a Black holes   Red dwarfs b
c Asteroids   Shooting stars d

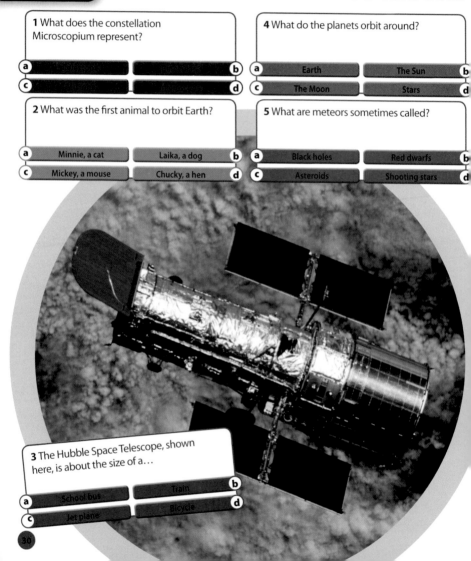

3 The Hubble Space Telescope, shown here, is about the size of a…

a School bus   Train b
c Jet plane   Bicycle d

6 ESA stands for European…

a Space Agent
b Special Astronaut
c Space Agency
d Space Administration

7 Which of these is not found on Venus's surface?

a Impact craters
b Mountains
c Lava plains
d Oceans

8 The distance between which two celestial bodies is known as an astronomical unit?

a Earth and the Sun
b The Sun and Neptune
c Earth and the Moon
d The Sun and Jupiter

9 Nothing can escape from this, not even light. What is this region called?

a Black hole
b Worm hole
c White hole
d Dumb hole

10 Who suggested in 1543 that Earth and the other planets revolve around the Sun?

a Aristotle
b Galileo Galilei
c Copernicus
d Plato

11 Which is the next stage in the Sun's life cycle?

a White dwarf
b Supernova
c Red giant
d Black hole

12 What is the name given to man-made objects that orbit Earth but are no longer in use?

a Satellites
b Robots
c Space shuttles
d Space debris

13 Which of these is a comet?

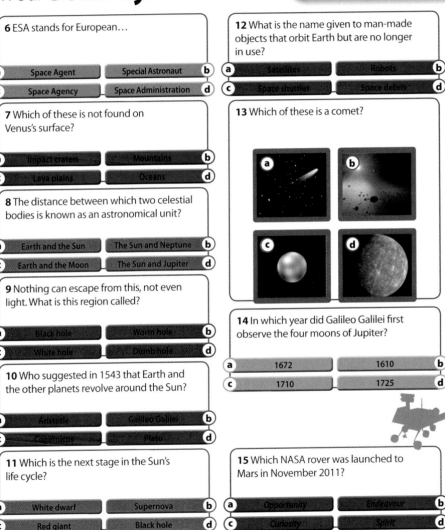

14 In which year did Galileo Galilei first observe the four moons of Jupiter?

a 1672
b 1610
c 1710
d 1725

15 Which NASA rover was launched to Mars in November 2011?

a Opportunity
b Endeavour
c Curiosity
d Spirit

31

14

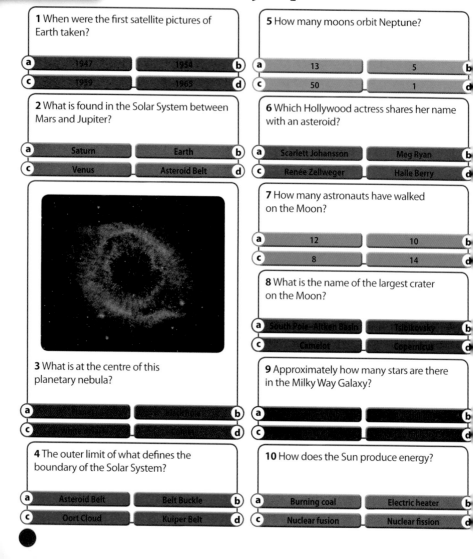

The volcano **Olympus Mons** is three

1 When were the first satellite pictures of Earth taken?

- **a** 1947
- **b** 1954
- **c** 1959
- **d** 1965

2 What is found in the Solar System between Mars and Jupiter?

- **a** Saturn
- **b** Earth
- **c** Venus
- **d** Asteroid Belt

3 What is at the centre of this planetary nebula?

- **a** Planet
- **b** Black hole
- **c** White dwarf
- **d** Comet

4 The outer limit of what defines the boundary of the Solar System?

- **a** Asteroid Belt
- **b** Belt Buckle
- **c** Oort Cloud
- **d** Kuiper Belt

5 How many moons orbit Neptune?

- **a** 13
- **b** 5
- **c** 50
- **d** 1

6 Which Hollywood actress shares her name with an asteroid?

- **a** Scarlett Johansson
- **b** Meg Ryan
- **c** Renée Zellweger
- **d** Halle Berry

7 How many astronauts have walked on the Moon?

- **a** 12
- **b** 10
- **c** 8
- **d** 14

8 What is the name of the largest crater on the Moon?

- **a** South Pole–Aitken Basin
- **b** Tsiolkovsky
- **c** Camelot
- **d** Copernicus

9 Approximately how many stars are there in the Milky Way Galaxy?

- **a**
- **b**
- **c**
- **d**

10 How does the Sun produce energy?

- **a** Burning coal
- **b** Electric heater
- **c** Nuclear fusion
- **d** Nuclear fission

11 Which constellation is depicted in the Australian flag?

a
b
c
d

12 Where on Mars did the rover *Spirit* land?

a
b
c
d

13 What is the approximate temperature at the core of the Sun?

a 10 million °C (18 million °F)
b 35 million °C (63 million °F)
c 20 million °C (36 million °F)
d 15 million °C (27 million °F)

14 Which kind of telescope are the twin Keck telescopes in Hawaii?

a
b
c
d

15 Which of these elements was not created in the Big Bang?

a
b
c
d

16 Which giant planet's density is less than that of water?

a Jupiter
b Uranus
c Saturn
d Neptune

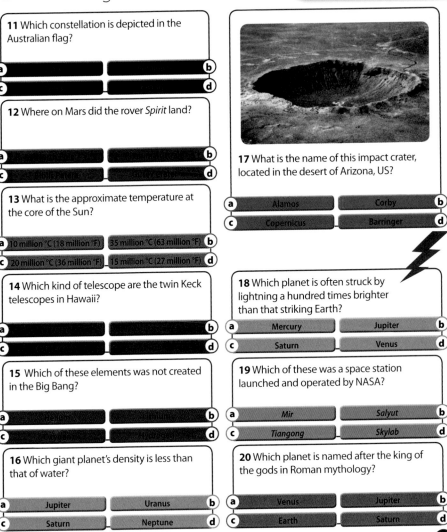

17 What is the name of this impact crater, located in the desert of Arizona, US?

a Alamos
b Corby
c Copernicus
d Barringer

18 Which planet is often struck by lightning a hundred times brighter than that striking Earth?

a Mercury
b Jupiter
c Saturn
d Venus

19 Which of these was a space station launched and operated by NASA?

a Mir
b Salyut
c Tiangong
d Skylab

20 Which planet is named after the king of the gods in Roman mythology?

a Venus
b Jupiter
c Earth
d Saturn

1 What is the temperature of the background heat from the Big Bang?

a
b
c
d

2 The stars in Orion's belt point to which star?

a Procyon, in Canis Minor
b Sirius, in Canis Major
c Castor, in Gemini
d Menkar, in Cetus

3 The planets follow paths in a band of Earth's sky based on the…

a Equator
b Meridian
c Pole
d Ecliptic

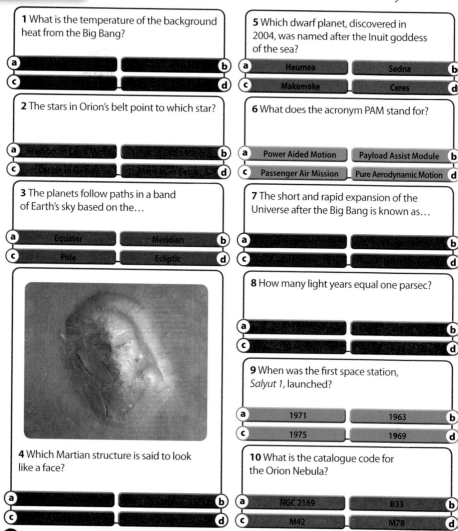

4 Which Martian structure is said to look like a face?

a
b
c
d

5 Which dwarf planet, discovered in 2004, was named after the Inuit goddess of the sea?

a Haumea
b Sedna
c Makemake
d Ceres

6 What does the acronym PAM stand for?

a Power Aided Motion
b Payload Assist Module
c Passenger Air Mission
d Pure Aerodynamic Motion

7 The short and rapid expansion of the Universe after the Big Bang is known as…

a
b
c
d

8 How many light years equal one parsec?

a
b
c
d

9 When was the first space station, *Salyut 1*, launched?

a 1971
b 1963
c 1975
d 1969

10 What is the catalogue code for the Orion Nebula?

a NGC 2169
b B33
c M42
d M78

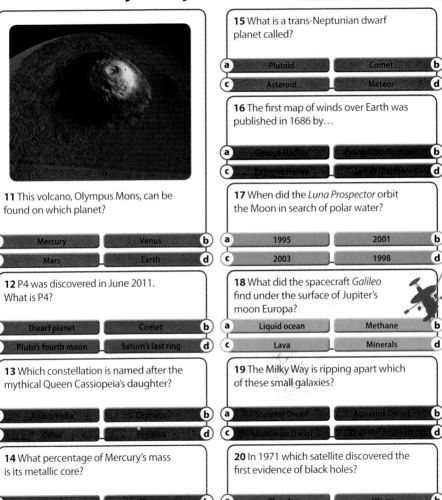

11 This volcano, Olympus Mons, can be found on which planet?

a. Mercury
b. Venus
c. Mars
d. Earth

12 P4 was discovered in June 2011. What is P4?

a. Dwarf planet
b. Comet
c. Pluto's fourth moon
d. Saturn's last ring

13 Which constellation is named after the mythical Queen Cassiopeia's daughter?

a. Andromeda
b. Cepheus
c. Cetus
d. Pegasus

14 What percentage of Mercury's mass is its metallic core?

a. 32–38 per cent
b. 58–63 per cent
c. 85–90 per cent
d. 65–70 per cent

15 What is a trans-Neptunian dwarf planet called?

a. Plutoid
b. Comet
c. Asteroid
d. Meteor

16 The first map of winds over Earth was published in 1686 by…

a. George Hadley
b. Evangelista Torricelli
c. Edmond Halley
d. James Glaisher

17 When did the *Luna Prospector* orbit the Moon in search of polar water?

a. 1995
b. 2001
c. 2003
d. 1998

18 What did the spacecraft *Galileo* find under the surface of Jupiter's moon Europa?

a. Liquid ocean
b. Methane
c. Lava
d. Minerals

19 The Milky Way is ripping apart which of these small galaxies?

a. Sculptor Dwarf
b. Aquarius Dwarf
c. Sagittarius Dwarf
d. Ursa Minor Dwarf

20 In 1971 which satellite discovered the first evidence of black holes?

a. Chandra
b. Uhuru
c. Rontgen
d. Rossi

Light from the Sun takes **8 minutes**,

1 Which comet has the shortest orbital period of 3.3 years?

a Encke
b Viscara
c Bennett
d Oterma

2 Which of the four rocky planets has the most moons?

a
b
c
d

3 About how many astronauts have been into space?

a 500
b 100
c 50
d 1,000

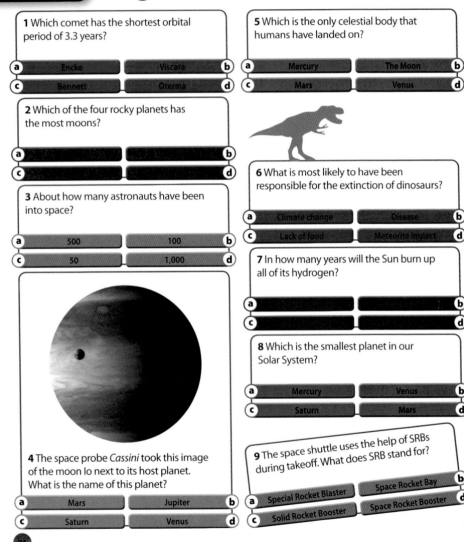

4 The space probe *Cassini* took this image of the moon Io next to its host planet. What is the name of this planet?

a Mars
b Jupiter
c Saturn
d Venus

5 Which is the only celestial body that humans have landed on?

a Mercury
b The Moon
c Mars
d Venus

6 What is most likely to have been responsible for the extinction of dinosaurs?

a Climate change
b Disease
c Lack of food
d Meteorite impact

7 In how many years will the Sun burn up all of its hydrogen?

a
b
c
d

8 Which is the smallest planet in our Solar System?

a Mercury
b Venus
c Saturn
d Mars

9 The space shuttle uses the help of SRBs during takeoff. What does SRB stand for?

a Special Rocket Blaster
b Space Rocket Bay
c Solid Rocket Booster
d Space Rocket Booster

18 seconds to reach us

10 The rotating chart used by stargazers to identify stars and constellations is called…

(a) [illegible]   (b) [illegible]

(c) [illegible]   (d) [illegible]

11 In 1961 "Ham" was sent into space. He came back to Earth with just a bruised nose. Ham was a…

(a) Horse   (b) Chimpanzee

(c) Man   (d) Pig

12 What gives Mars its distinctive red colour?

(a) Copper-rich soil   (b) Red clouds

(c) Iron-oxide-rich soil   (d) High temperature

13 Who proved that Copernicus's theory of planets revolving around the Sun was correct?

(a) Johannes Kepler   (b) Isaac Newton

(c) Edmond Halley   (d) Galileo Galilei

14 Venus appears so bright from Earth because it is…

(a) A former star   (b) Part of a constellation

(c) Closest to the Sun   (d) Closest the Earth

15 How many zodiac constellations are there?

(a) [illegible]   (b) [illegible]

(c) [illegible]   (d) [illegible]

37

1 What are Saturn's rings composed of?

a Rock boulders
b Dust
c Gases
d Icy fragments

2 The first satellite to transmit pictures of Earth from space was…

a Explorer 16
b Explorer 6
c Explorer 2
d Explorer 11

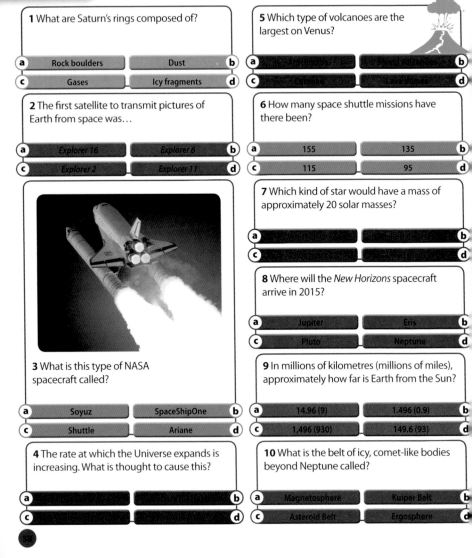

3 What is this type of NASA spacecraft called?

a Soyuz
b SpaceShipOne
c Shuttle
d Ariane

4 The rate at which the Universe expands is increasing. What is thought to cause this?

a
b
c
d

5 Which type of volcanoes are the largest on Venus?

a Arachnoids
b Shield volcanoes
c Coronae
d Lava domes

6 How many space shuttle missions have there been?

a 155
b 135
c 115
d 95

7 Which kind of star would have a mass of approximately 20 solar masses?

a
b
c
d

8 Where will the *New Horizons* spacecraft arrive in 2015?

a Jupiter
b Eris
c Pluto
d Neptune

9 In millions of kilometres (millions of miles), approximately how far is Earth from the Sun?

a 14.96 (9)
b 1.496 (0.9)
c 1,496 (930)
d 149.6 (93)

10 What is the belt of icy, comet-like bodies beyond Neptune called?

a Magnetosphere
b Kuiper Belt
c Asteroid Belt
d Ergosphere

identified by **name** or number

11 Which is the second largest planet in the Solar System?

a Saturn | b Neptune
c Uranus | d Jupiter

12 Which Academy-award winning actor has an asteroid named after him?

a Tom Hanks | b Matt Damon
c Daniel Day-Lewis | d Denzel Washington

13 What is 96.5 per cent of Venus's atmosphere made up of?

a Carbon dioxide | b Sulphur dioxide
c Nitrogen | d Helium

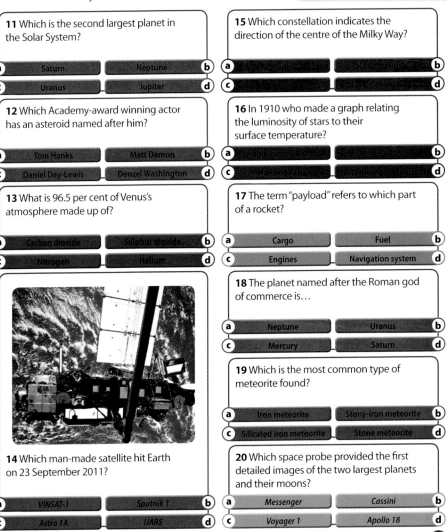

14 Which man-made satellite hit Earth on 23 September 2011?

a VINSAT-1 | b Sputnik 1
c Astra 1A | d UARS

15 Which constellation indicates the direction of the centre of the Milky Way?

a | b
c | d

16 In 1910 who made a graph relating the luminosity of stars to their surface temperature?

a | b
c | d

17 The term "payload" refers to which part of a rocket?

a Cargo | b Fuel
c Engines | d Navigation system

18 The planet named after the Roman god of commerce is…

a Neptune | b Uranus
c Mercury | d Saturn

19 Which is the most common type of meteorite found?

a Iron meteorite | b Stony-iron meteorite
c Silicated iron meteorite | d Stone meteorite

20 Which space probe provided the first detailed images of the two largest planets and their moons?

a Messenger | b Cassini
c Voyager 1 | d Apollo 18

1 The Babylonians associated which planet with Nergal, their god of war and the underworld?

- **a** Mercury
- **b** Jupiter
- **c** Mars
- **d** Venus

2 Who or what are Zvezda and Kibo?

- **a** Communication satellites
- **b** Two ISS modules
- **c** Dogs sent into space
- **d** First Japanese astronauts

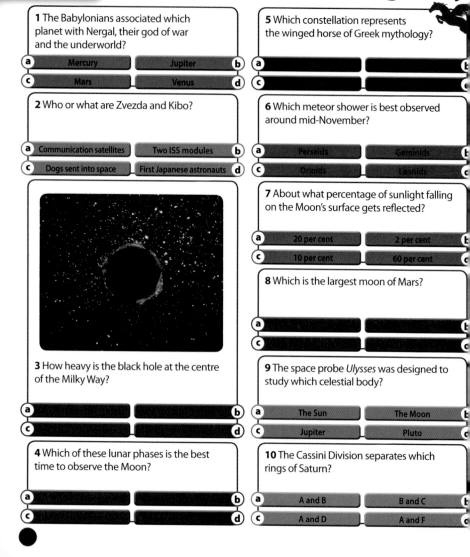

3 How heavy is the black hole at the centre of the Milky Way?

- **a**
- **b**
- **c**
- **d**

4 Which of these lunar phases is the best time to observe the Moon?

- **a**
- **b**
- **c**
- **d**

5 Which constellation represents the winged horse of Greek mythology?

- **a**
- **b**
- **c**
- **d**

6 Which meteor shower is best observed around mid-November?

- **a** Perseids
- **b** Geminids
- **c** Orinids
- **d** Leonids

7 About what percentage of sunlight falling on the Moon's surface gets reflected?

- **a** 20 per cent
- **b** 2 per cent
- **c** 10 per cent
- **d** 60 per cent

8 Which is the largest moon of Mars?

- **a**
- **b**
- **c**
- **d**

9 The space probe *Ulysses* was designed to study which celestial body?

- **a** The Sun
- **b** The Moon
- **c** Jupiter
- **d** Pluto

10 The Cassini Division separates which rings of Saturn?

- **a** A and B
- **b** B and C
- **c** A and D
- **d** A and F

11 Which *Explorer* satellite is equipped to probe the icy temperatures of deep space?

a

b

c

d

12 Which satellite carried the first instruments to study climate?

a

b

c

d

13 What is the apparent magnitude of Sirius?

a

b

c

d

14 Which particles began forming about one microsecond after the Big Bang?

a

b

c

d

15 When was Pluto's fourth moon, P4, discovered?

a September 2009

b August 2005

c June 2011

d May 2010

16 Which planet's moons are named after Shakespearian characters such as Oberon, Titania, and Puck?

a Uranus

b Jupiter

c Mars

d Neptune

17 Which spacecraft performed the first successful flyby of Mars?

a Mariner 3

b Mariner 2

c Mariner 1

d Mariner 4

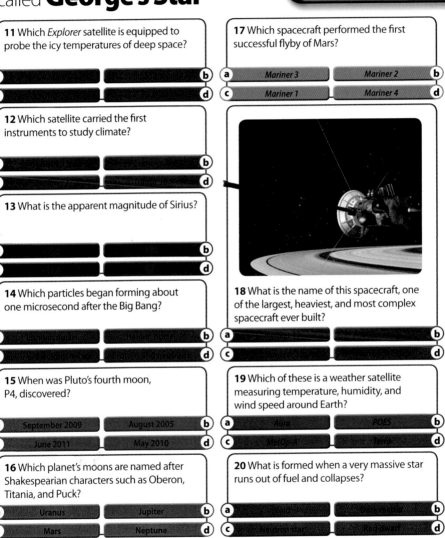

18 What is the name of this spacecraft, one of the largest, heaviest, and most complex spacecraft ever built?

a

b

c

d

19 Which of these is a weather satellite measuring temperature, humidity, and wind speed around Earth?

a Aura

b POES

c MetOp-A

d Terra

20 What is formed when a very massive star runs out of fuel and collapses?

a Void

b Dark matter

c Neutron star

d Red dwarf

Nobody has been on the

1 Which was the first artificial satellite to be put into Earth's orbit?

- **a** Sputnik 1
- **b** Explorer 1
- **c** Pioneer 1
- **d** Vanguard 1

2 Who directed the 2005 film *War of the Worlds*?

- **a**
- **b**
- **c**
- **d**

3 Which was the first comet to be seen in close-up?

- **a** West
- **b** Halley
- **c** Encke
- **d** Hale–Bopp

4 Which planet has the most moons?

- **a** Venus
- **b** Neptune
- **c** Jupiter
- **d** Earth

5 There are astronauts working above us now in space for weeks or even months at a time. Where do they live?

- **a** On the Moon
- **b** On Mars
- **c** In a shuttle
- **d** On a space station

6 Which novel by H G Wells about an alien invasion from Mars was published in 1898?

- **a** The World is Not Enough
- **b** The War of the Worlds
- **c** Brave New World
- **d** The Way of the World

7 Approximately what percentage of Earth's surface is covered with water?

- **a** 70 per cent
- **b** 84 per cent
- **c** 45 per cent
- **d** 65 per cent

8 Which is the only planet whose name is not derived from Roman or Greek mythology?

- **a** Mars
- **b** Neptune
- **c** Venus
- **d** Earth

9 At the end of its life, the Sun will become a…

Red giant

White dwarf (b)

Supernova

Black hole (d)

12 Neil Armstrong was the first person to do what?

(a) Orbit Earth

Write science fiction (b)

(c) Walk on the Moon

Visit Venus (d)

13 How many rings does Uranus have?

(a) 2

20 (b)

(c) 13

5 (d)

10 What binds galaxies into clusters like these?

Light

Energy (b)

Dark matter

Radiation (d)

14 How many astronauts have walked on the Moon?

(a) 12

23 (b)

(c) 41

35 (d)

11 The constellation Draco represents a…

Dragon (b)

(d)

15 The planet Mars was named *Her Desher* by the Egyptians. What does this mean?

(a) Dark one

Giant one (b)

(c) Ringed one

Red one (d)

Ganymede, Jupiter's largest **moon,**

1 Frozen water and which other major component make up the Martian polar caps?

a	Helium	Dry ice	**b**
c	Methane	Nitrogen	**d**

2 How do stars produce energy?

a			**b**
c			**d**

3 About how many spacewalks have astronauts made?

a	700	500	**b**
c	300	900	**d**

4 What caused the solar nebula to contract and spin faster?

a			**b**
c			**d**

5 Neso, the most distant moon of any Solar System planet, orbits which planet?

a	Neptune	Saturn	**b**
c	Jupiter	Uranus	**d**

6 Which planet passes between Earth and the Sun approximately 14 times each century?

a			**b**
c			**d**

7 Since 1972 which series of satellites have been photographing Earth's continents and coasts?

a			**b**
c			**d**

8 When was the Kuiper Belt discovered?

a	1983	1987	**b**
c	1990	1992	**d**

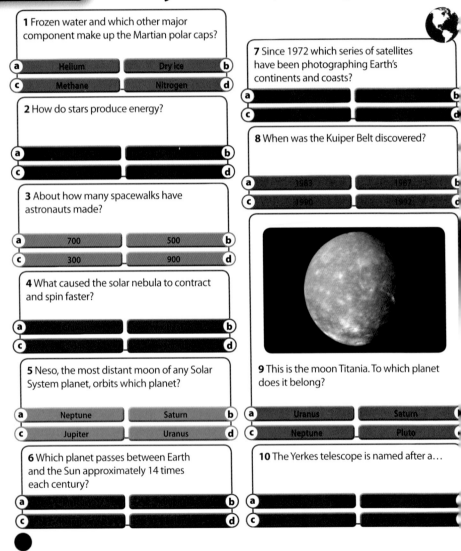

9 This is the moon Titania. To which planet does it belong?

a	Uranus	Saturn	**b**
c	Neptune	Pluto	**d**

10 The Yerkes telescope is named after a…

a		
c		

11 The phenomenon of the coming together of rocks to form Earth is called…

a Accretion disk

b Accreditation

c Cold accretion

d Hot accretion

12 Which of these is the nearest large cluster of galaxies to the Local Group?

a

b

c

d

13 Small moons that orbit near the edge of a planet's rings are called…

a Natural satellites

b Shepherd satellites

c Trojan moons

d Galilean satellites

14 Which pair of rovers landed on Mars in 2004?

a

b

c

d

15 Spacewalks are officially referred to as EVA. What does EVA stand for?

a Extra-vehicular Access

b Extra-vehicular Ability

c Extra-vehicular Action

d Extra-vehicular Activity

16 Which of the following refers to a star in its early stage of formation?

a

b

c

d

17 What is the name of this space station, which was a collaboration of 16 nations?

a Salyut

b International Space Station

c Mir

d Skylab

18 How many moons does the dwarf planet Haumea have?

a 3

b 1

c 2

d None

19 Volcanoes on which celestial body spew ice rather than molten rock?

a Leda

b Rhea

c Titan

d Erinome

20 The Earth to Moon mass ratio is…

a 50:1

b 120:1

c 141:1

d 81:1

1 How is the mass–energy of the Universe divided between ordinary matter (OM), dark matter (DM), and dark energy (DE)?

(a) ⬛ (b)
(c) ⬛ (d)

2 What is Alexei Leonov's claim to fame? He was the first to…

(a) Orbit Earth (b) Walk in space
(c) Perform a space repair (d) Take a photo from space

3 The findings of which satellite between 1989 and 1993 resulted in two major catalogues of stars?

(a) ⬛ (b)
(c) ⬛ (d)

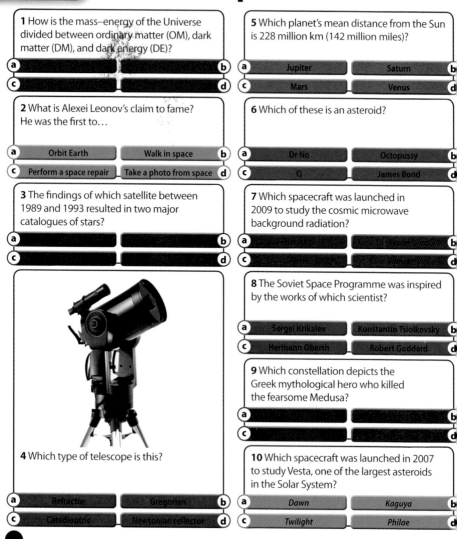

4 Which type of telescope is this?

(a) Refractor (b) Gregorian
(c) Catadioptric (d) Newtonian reflector

5 Which planet's mean distance from the Sun is 228 million km (142 million miles)?

(a) Jupiter (b) Saturn
(c) Mars (d) Venus

6 Which of these is an asteroid?

(a) Dr No (b) Octopussy
(c) Q (d) James Bond

7 Which spacecraft was launched in 2009 to study the cosmic microwave background radiation?

(a) ⬛ (b)
(c) ⬛ (d)

8 The Soviet Space Programme was inspired by the works of which scientist?

(a) Sergei Krikalev (b) Konstantin Tsiolkovsky
(c) Hermann Oberth (d) Robert Goddard

9 Which constellation depicts the Greek mythological hero who killed the fearsome Medusa?

(a) ⬛ (b)
(c) ⬛ (d)

10 Which spacecraft was launched in 2007 to study Vesta, one of the largest asteroids in the Solar System?

(a) Dawn (b) Kaguya
(c) Twilight (d) Philae

11 Which of Saturn's rings is the broadest?

a F ring
b A ring
c B ring
d D ring

12 British pop group The Tornadoes had a hit song named after a communication satellite. Which satellite?

a TIROS
b Vanguard
c Orbita
d Telstar

13 Who discovered the moons of Mars?

a Asaph Hall
b Johann Bode
c Caroline Herschel
d Wilhelm Beer

14 Asteroids that share their orbits with a planet or a moon are called…

a Dwarf
b Collision
c Trojan
d Planetary

15 What are GRBs?

a Galaxy Record Books
b Gravity Record Books
c Gamma Ray Bursts
d Great Radiation Bursts

16 Long fissures of ice called tiger stripes are found on which of Saturn's moons?

a Enceladus
b Tethys
c Hyperion
d Rhea

17 Which of these birds does not share its name with a constellation?

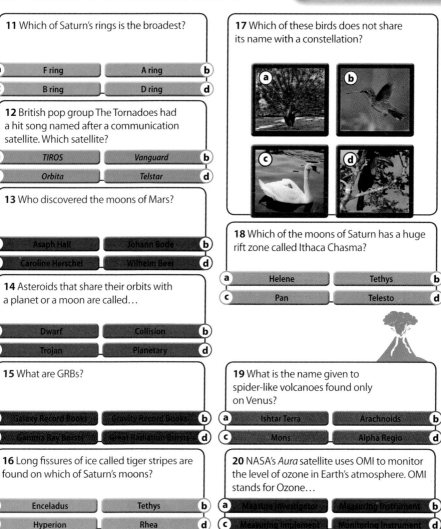

a
b
c
d

18 Which of the moons of Saturn has a huge rift zone called Ithaca Chasma?

a Helene
b Tethys
c Pan
d Telesto

19 What is the name given to spider-like volcanoes found only on Venus?

a Ishtar Terra
b Arachnoids
c Mons
d Alpha Regio

20 NASA's *Aura* satellite uses OMI to monitor the level of ozone in Earth's atmosphere. OMI stands for Ozone…

a Measure Investigator
b Measuring Instrument
c Measuring Implement
d Monitoring Instrument

1 What was the name of the first spacecraft to take men to the surface of the Moon?

a
b
c
d

2 Which of these is not a planet?

a Pluto
b Jupiter
c Venus
d Neptune

3 Pluto's largest moon is called Charon. In Greek mythology, who was Charon?

a A sea nymph
b Ferryman of the dead
c Gatekeeper to hell
d God of the underworld

4 Which James Bond film featured Roger Moore and made the space shuttle a big-screen icon?

a
b
c
d

5 When might a lunar eclipse occur?

a On a new Moon day
b Once a month
c Once a decade
d On a full Moon day

6 Which day of the week is named after the Moon?

a Wednesday
b Friday
c Monday
d Sunday

7 The first spacewalk was performed by…

a Svetlana Savitskaya
b Jean-Loup Chrétien
c Alexei Leonov
d Ed White

8 Which gas is responsible for making Venus very hot?

a
b
c
d

9 What is a taikonaut?

a Animal astronaut
b Russian rocket
c Japanese shuttle
d Chinese astronaut

10 Stars in the Plough (Big Dipper) make up part of which constellation?

a
b
c
d

11 The Sun is located in which arm of the Milky Way?

a
b
c
d

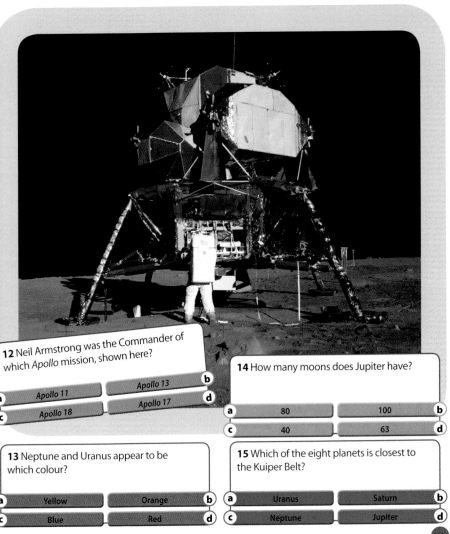

12 Neil Armstrong was the Commander of which *Apollo* mission, shown here?

- **a** Apollo 11
- **b** Apollo 13
- **c** Apollo 18
- **d** Apollo 17

13 Neptune and Uranus appear to be which colour?

- **a** Yellow
- **b** Orange
- **c** Blue
- **d** Red

14 How many moons does Jupiter have?

- **a** 80
- **b** 100
- **c** 40
- **d** 63

15 Which of the eight planets is closest to the Kuiper Belt?

- **a** Uranus
- **b** Saturn
- **c** Neptune
- **d** Jupiter

23

British astronomer **Fred Hoyle**

1 Which was the first planet to be discovered by mathematical calculations rather than actual observations of the sky?

- **a** Uranus
- **b** Saturn
- **c** Neptune
- **d** Pluto

2 The giant impact theory suggests the Moon was once part of which planetary body?

- **a** Mars
- **b** Venus
- **c** Mercury
- **d** Earth

3 About how many stars does a typical galaxy have?

- **a** 100 billion
- **b** 100 million
- **c** 1 billion
- **d** 1 million

4 A star pattern made from some stars of a constellation, or stars from more than one constellation, is called an…

- **a**
- **b**
- **c** Asterisk
- **d** Anomaly

5 How old was the Universe when Earth was formed?

- **a** 7 billion years
- **b** 5 billion years
- **c** 10 billion years
- **d** 9 billion years

6 What is the *Kepler* mission looking for?

- **a** Black holes
- **b** New stars
- **c** Exoplanets
- **d** Binary stars

7 Which potato-shaped moon of Mars is heavily cratered?

- **a** Deimos
- **b** Ymir
- **c** Janus
- **d** Phobos

8 Where on the Sun does nuclear reaction take place?

- **a** Chromosphere
- **b** Core
- **c** Convection zone
- **d** Radiative zone

9 What would you associate the names Apollo, Amor, and Aten with?

- **a** Lunar missions
- **b** Space shuttles
- **c** Comets
- **d** Asteroids

10 In space exploration, what is a fairing?

- **a** Microsatellite
- **b** Aerodynamic shell
- **c** Shuttle's main engine
- **d** Ginger biscuit

11 Which planet's axis is the least tilted?

a Jupiter
b Uranus
c Mercury
d Venus

12 The only living creature to have been killed by a meteorite was an…

a English cat
b Indian tiger
c Egyptian dog
d American porcupine

13 Which of these astronauts has accumulated more than 50 hours of spacewalking?

a Michael Gernhardt
b Dominic Gorie
c John Grunsfeld
d William Gregory

14 What is the centre of a black hole called?

a Frank
b Ergosphere
c Singularity
d Event horizon

15 How many moons orbit Saturn?

a 65
b 62
c 71
d 51

16 Which planet's total surface area equals the total land area of Earth?

a Mars
b Venus
c Mercury
d Uranus

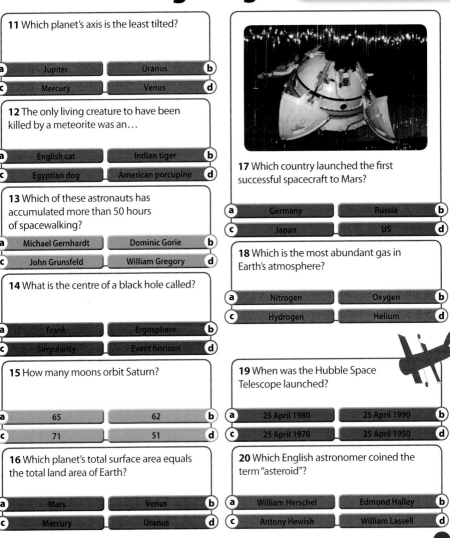

17 Which country launched the first successful spacecraft to Mars?

a Germany
b Russia
c Japan
d US

18 Which is the most abundant gas in Earth's atmosphere?

a Nitrogen
b Oxygen
c Hydrogen
d Helium

19 When was the Hubble Space Telescope launched?

a 25 April 1980
b 25 April 1990
c 25 April 1970
d 25 April 1950

20 Which English astronomer coined the term "asteroid"?

a William Herschel
b Edmond Halley
c Antony Hewish
d William Lassell

1 The dwarf planet Haumea is named after the Hawaiian goddess of…

a Fertility and childbirth | b Lust
c Wealth | d Rain

2 Who invented the term "black hole"?

a John Wheeler | b Hermann Bondi
c Fred Hoyle | d Tommy Gold

3 Which French astronomer made a catalogue of about 100 of the brightest nebulae in 1784?

a Henrietta Leavitt | b Williams Huggins
c Bernard Lyot | d Charles Messier

4 The layer of dust and rock fragments covering the surface of a planet is called…

a Plasma | b Regolith
c Photosphere | d Atmosphere

5 Which is the largest known structure in the Universe?

a Shapley Concentration | b Hercules Supercluster
c Columba Cluster | d Sloan Great Wall

6 The *Apollo* spacecraft consisted of three modules: the command module, the lunar module, and the…

a Blast module | b Service module
c Landing module | d Escape module

7 How much hydrogen does the Sun burn every second?

a 400 million tonnes | b 250 million tonnes
c 300 million tonnes | d 600 million tonnes

8 When was the Solar and Heliospheric Observatory (SOHO), a joint project by NASA and the ESA, launched?

a 1990 | b 1995
c 1989 | d 2000

9 Which Mars rover was inducted into the Robot Hall of Fame in 2003?

a Sojourner | b Spirit
c Opportunity | d Curiosity

10 Type C, Type S, and Type M are categories of what?

a Natural satellites | b Dwarf planets
c Asteroids | d Comets

11 The Keystone asterism is from which constellation?

a Pegasus

b Aries

c Ursa Minor

d Hercules

12 Voltaire and Swift craters are found on which planet's moon?

a Earth

b Mercury

c Venus

d Mars

13 Massive stars on the verge of supernovae explosions are called...

a Red giants

b Protostars

c Wolf-Rayet stars

d T-Tauri stars

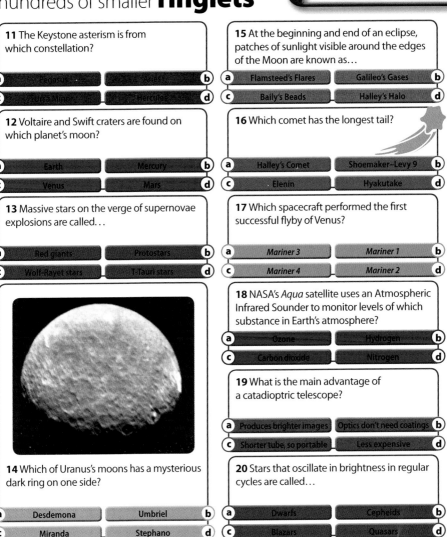

14 Which of Uranus's moons has a mysterious dark ring on one side?

a Desdemona

b Umbriel

c Miranda

d Stephano

15 At the beginning and end of an eclipse, patches of sunlight visible around the edges of the Moon are known as...

a Flamsteed's Flares

b Galileo's Gases

c Baily's Beads

d Halley's Halo

16 Which comet has the longest tail?

a Halley's Comet

b Shoemaker–Levy 9

c Elenin

d Hyakutake

17 Which spacecraft performed the first successful flyby of Venus?

a *Mariner 3*

b *Mariner 1*

c *Mariner 4*

d *Mariner 2*

18 NASA's *Aqua* satellite uses an Atmospheric Infrared Sounder to monitor levels of which substance in Earth's atmosphere?

a Ozone

b Hydrogen

c Carbon dioxide

d Nitrogen

19 What is the main advantage of a catadioptric telescope?

a Produces brighter images

b Optics don't need coatings

c Shorter tube, so portable

d Less expensive

20 Stars that oscillate in brightness in regular cycles are called...

a Dwarfs

b Cepheids

c Blazars

d Quasars

The **Sun** contains **99.8** per cent

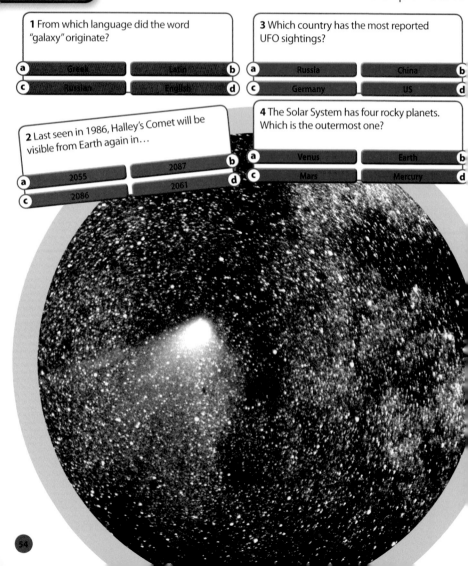

1 From which language did the word "galaxy" originate?

a Greek
b Latin
c Russian
d English

2 Last seen in 1986, Halley's Comet will be visible from Earth again in…

a 2055
b 2087
c 2086
d 2061

3 Which country has the most reported UFO sightings?

a Russia
b China
c Germany
d US

4 The Solar System has four rocky planets. Which is the outermost one?

a Venus
b Earth
c Mars
d Mercury

5 In *The Simpsons* which character destroys an ant farm in space?

a Homer Simpson **b** Sideshow Bob
c Mayor Quimby **d** Mr Burns

6 Which day of the week is named after the Sun?

a Tuesday **b** Friday
c Sunday **d** Monday

7 Which astronaut walked on the Moon with Neil Armstrong in 1969?

a Ken Mattingly **b** Buzz Aldrin
c Michael Collins **d** Jim Lovell

8 Which two planets lie between Earth and the Sun?

a Mars and Saturn **b** Mercury and Venus
c Mercury and Mars **d** Venus and Mars

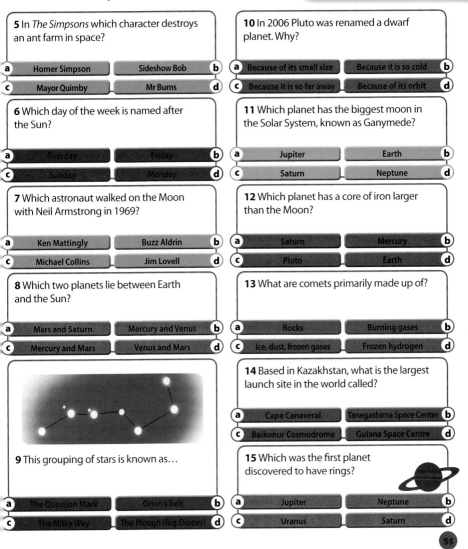

9 This grouping of stars is known as…

a The Question Mark **b** Orion's Belt
c The Milky Way **d** The Plough (Big Dipper)

10 In 2006 Pluto was renamed a dwarf planet. Why?

a Because of its small size **b** Because it is so cold
c Because it is so far away **d** Because of its orbit

11 Which planet has the biggest moon in the Solar System, known as Ganymede?

a Jupiter **b** Earth
c Saturn **d** Neptune

12 Which planet has a core of iron larger than the Moon?

a Saturn **b** Mercury
c Pluto **d** Earth

13 What are comets primarily made up of?

a Rocks **b** Burning gases
c Ice, dust, frozen gases **d** Frozen hydrogen

14 Based in Kazakhstan, what is the largest launch site in the world called?

a Cape Canaveral **b** Tanegashima Space Center
c Baikonur Cosmodrome **d** Guiana Space Centre

15 Which was the first planet discovered to have rings?

a Jupiter **b** Neptune
c Uranus **d** Saturn

1 What is Neptune's largest moon called?

- **a** Triton
- **b** Naiad
- **c** Proteus
- **d** Nereid

2 Which planet is the smallest of the giant planets?

- **a** Uranus
- **b** Neptune
- **c** Jupiter
- **d** Saturn

3 An abnormal warming of surface ocean waters in the eastern tropical Pacific Ocean is called…

- **a** La Niña
- **b** El Hombre
- **c** El Viejo
- **d** El Niño

4 Which star is also known as the Dog Star?

- **a**
- **b**
- **c**
- **d**

5 In 2011 astronomers determined the average colour of the Milky Way Galaxy. They described it as…

- **a** Ocean-spray white
- **b** Buttermilk cream
- **c** Morning-snow white
- **d** Fire-smoke grey

6 About 75 per cent of all asteroids are…

- **a** Gaseous
- **b** Carbonaceous
- **c** Silicaceous
- **d** Metallic

7 *Salyut* was so named to give a salute of honour to…

- **a** Yuri Gagarin
- **b** Vladimir Lenin
- **c** Nikita Khrushchev
- **d** Leonid Brezhnev

8 Who was the first woman to discover a comet?

- **a** Dorrit Hoffleit
- **b** Antonia Maury
- **c** Caroline Herschel
- **d** Maria Mitchell

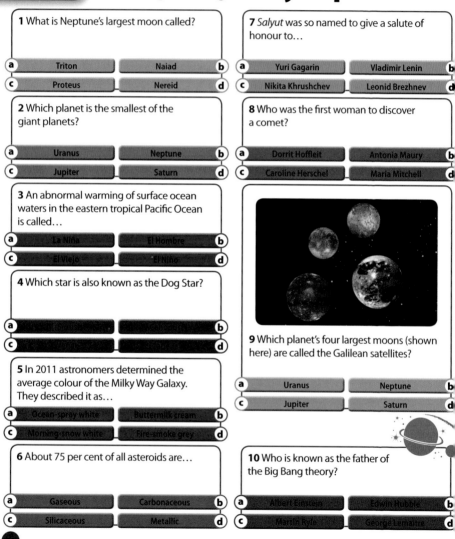

9 Which planet's four largest moons (shown here) are called the Galilean satellites?

- **a** Uranus
- **b** Neptune
- **c** Jupiter
- **d** Saturn

10 Who is known as the father of the Big Bang theory?

- **a** Albert Einstein
- **b** Edwin Hubble
- **c** Martin Ryle
- **d** George Lemaitre

Difficulty level: **Medium**

11 Moon rocks are mostly which type of rock?

a Metamorphic
b Layered
c Igneous
d Sedimentary

12 What is a galaxy with a bright core known as?

a Whirlpool galaxy
b Cartwheel galaxy
c Active galaxy
d Starburst galaxy

13 Which is the only spacecraft to have explored Neptune?

a Messenger
b Cassini
c Pioneer 10
d Voyager 2

14 Launched in 2005, the most recent probe sent to Venus was…

a Venus Express
b Voyager 2
c Cassini
d Mariner

15 Which planet has the shortest orbit?

a Venus
b Earth
c Mars
d Mercury

16 Towards the end of its life, what does a main sequence star turn into?

a Supernova
b Planetary nebula
c Brown dwarf
d Black hole

17 Which planet has 13 known rings encircling it?

a Neptune
b Uranus
c Saturn
d Jupiter

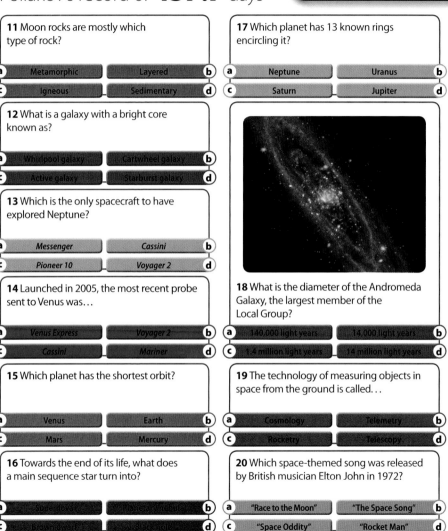

18 What is the diameter of the Andromeda Galaxy, the largest member of the Local Group?

a 140,000 light years
b 14,000 light years
c 1.4 million light years
d 14 million light years

19 The technology of measuring objects in space from the ground is called…

a Cosmology
b Telemetry
c Rocketry
d Telescopy

20 Which space-themed song was released by British musician Elton John in 1972?

a "Race to the Moon"
b "The Space Song"
c "Space Oddity"
d "Rocket Man"

57

1 Which theory states that the Universe has no beginning and no end?

a Steady State theory
b Hubble's Law
c Top Down theory
d Bottom Up theory

2 The highest response to a NASA job advert for astronauts was in 1978. How many people applied?

a 8,000
b 5,000
c 2,500
d 11,300

3 Which satellite monitors Earth's polar ice sheets?

a Landsat
b EOS
c Nimbus
d Cryosat 2

4 Which is the largest satellite of the dwarf planet Pluto?

a Charon
b Nix
c Hydra
d S/2011 P1

5 What telescope aperture is needed to view objects of an apparent magnitude of 14.7?

a 200mm (8in)
b 150mm (6in)
c 100mm (4in)
d 250mm (10in)

6 Which of Uranus's moons are called shepherd moons?

a Juliet and Portia
b Belinda and Perdita
c Cordelia and Ophelia
d Ariel and Francisco

7 Comets that come extremely close to the Sun are called…

a Edgeworth Bodies
b Nakajima Rangers
c Bell Comets
d Kreutz Sungrazers

8 What is the axial tilt of Uranus?

a 29.6°
b 177.3°
c 97.9°
d 23.5°

9 The first systematic naming of stars was introduced in 1603. Who introduced it?

a John Flamsteed
b Charles Messier
c Galileo Galilei
d Johann Bayer

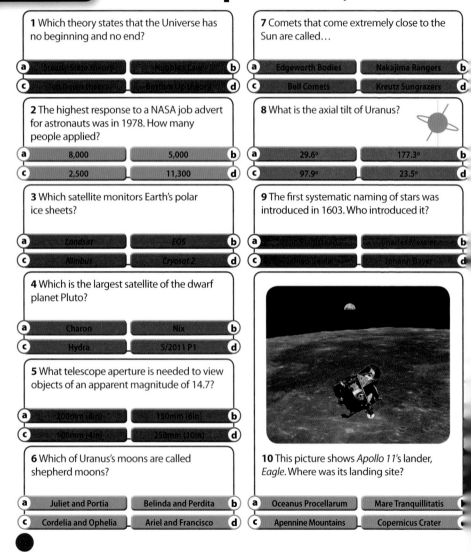

10 This picture shows *Apollo 11*'s lander, *Eagle*. Where was its landing site?

a Oceanus Procellarum
b Mare Tranquillitatis
c Apennine Mountains
d Copernicus Crater

11 How long does the Sun take to rotate on its axis?

17.8 days	25.4 days (b)
22.5 days	28 days (d)

12 Which of Saturn's moons has an irregular-shaped, sponge-like appearance?

Titan	Hyperion (b)
Dione	Iapetus (d)

13 The *Deep Impact* probe was designed to study the interior of which comet?

Hale–Bopp Comet	Borrelly's Comet (b)
Tempel 1 Comet	Halley's Comet (d)

14 Extremely luminous stars that have exhausted the hydrogen fuel in their cores are called…

Red giants	White giants (b)
Blue giants	Brown giants (d)

15 How fast must a spacecraft move to escape Earth's gravitational pull?

11kps (7mps)	15kps (9mps) (b)
8kps (5mps)	10kps (6mps) (d)

16 Which is the biggest canyon system in the Solar System?

Valles Marineris	Uranius Tholus (b)
Arsia Mons	Grand Canyon (d)

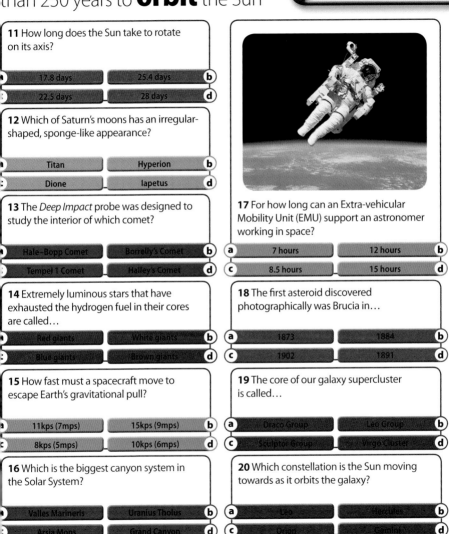

17 For how long can an Extra-vehicular Mobility Unit (EMU) support an astronomer working in space?

(a) 7 hours	12 hours (b)
(c) 8.5 hours	15 hours (d)

18 The first asteroid discovered photographically was Brucia in…

(a) 1873	1884 (b)
(c) 1902	1891 (d)

19 The core of our galaxy supercluster is called…

(a) Draco Group	Leo Group (b)
(c) Sculptor Group	Virgo Cluster (d)

20 Which constellation is the Sun moving towards as it orbits the galaxy?

(a) Leo	Hercules (b)
(c) Orion	Gemini (d)

The **Milky Way** is about

1 What do the four planets closest to the Sun have in common?

- (a) They are made of rock
- (b) They have rings
- (c) They have life on them
- (d) They are made of gas

2 Which is the closest star to the Sun?

- (a) Mercury
- (b) Alpha Centauri
- (c) Sirius
- (d) Proxima Centauri

3 Which constellation represents the "water bearer"?

- (a)
- (b)
- (c)
- (d)

4 How many edges does the Universe have?

- (a)
- (b)
- (c)
- (d)

5 Spacecraft launch sites should ideally be located very close to the…

- (a) North Pole
- (b) Tropic of Capricorn
- (c) Tropic of Cancer
- (d) Equator

6 Who wrote *The Time Machine*?

- (a) Orson Welles
- (b) H G Wells
- (c) Stephen Hawking
- (d) Richard Dawkins

7 Which one of Jupiter's moons is larger than the planet Mercury?

- (a) Amalthea
- (b) Ganymede
- (c) Adrastea
- (d) Io

8 Which comet, shown here, made for a spectacular sight in 1997?

- (a) Hale–Bopp Comet
- (b) Halley's Comet
- (c) McNaught Comet
- (d) Bennett Comet

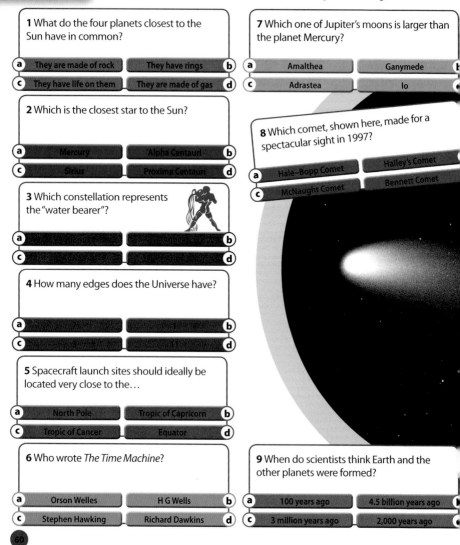

9 When do scientists think Earth and the other planets were formed?

- (a) 100 years ago
- (b) 4.5 billion years ago
- (c) 3 million years ago
- (d) 2,000 years ago

10 The poles of which planet, apart from Earth, have frozen water?

a Mercury
b Saturn
c Mars
d Venus

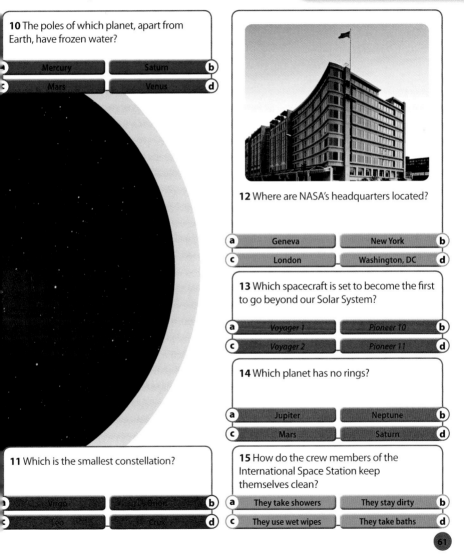

11 Which is the smallest constellation?

a Virgo
b Orion
c Leo
d Crux

12 Where are NASA's headquarters located?

a Geneva
b New York
c London
d Washington, DC

13 Which spacecraft is set to become the first to go beyond our Solar System?

a Voyager 1
b Pioneer 10
c Voyager 2
d Pioneer 11

14 Which planet has no rings?

a Jupiter
b Neptune
c Mars
d Saturn

15 How do the crew members of the International Space Station keep themselves clean?

a They take showers
b They stay dirty
c They use wet wipes
d They take baths

At 25, Gherman Titov was the **youngest**

1 Three lunar roving vehicles were taken to the Moon between 1971 and 1972. What happened to them?

(a) They are in museums
(b) They were destroyed
(c) They are still on the Moon
(d) They were lost

2 When did Edwin Hubble, pictured here, discover that the Universe is expanding?

(a) 1929
(b) 1923
(c) 1935
(d) 1930

3 Who became the first female spacewalker?

(a) Anna Fisher
(b) Svetlana Savitskaya
(c) Kalpana Chawla
(d) Catherine Coleman

4 Which planet has the most extreme temperatures?

(a) Mars
(b) Mercury
(c) Venus
(d) Jupiter

5 Which robotic space probe was jointly launched by NASA and ESA to study the Sun?

(a) Apollo
(b) Soyuz
(c) Ulysses
(d) Gemini

6 What was the name of Europe's first spacecraft to Mars?

(a) Mars Express
(b) Pioneer 5
(c) Mars 1
(d) Mariner 1

7 What are stars with tremendous mass and luminosity called?

(a)
(b)
(c)
(d)

8 What indicates that part of Earth's core is made of iron?

(a) Earth's weight
(b) Rust
(c) Heat
(d) Earth's magnetic field

9 The meteor shower Perseids peaks around the middle of which month?

(a) August
(b) November
(c) December
(d) September

10 The Great Dark Spot was a short-lived but gigantic storm on which planet?

(a) Saturn
(b) Neptune
(c) Jupiter
(d) Uranus

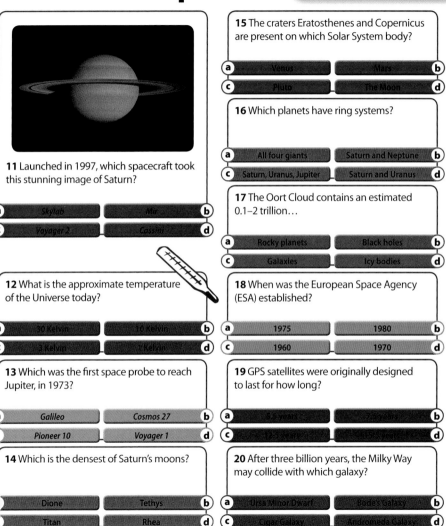

11 Launched in 1997, which spacecraft took this stunning image of Saturn?

Skylab	**b** Mir
Voyager 2	**d** Cassini

12 What is the approximate temperature of the Universe today?

30 Kelvin	**b** 10 Kelvin
3 Kelvin	**d** 1 Kelvin

13 Which was the first space probe to reach Jupiter, in 1973?

Galileo	**b** Cosmos 27
Pioneer 10	**d** Voyager 1

14 Which is the densest of Saturn's moons?

Dione	**b** Tethys
Titan	**d** Rhea

15 The craters Eratosthenes and Copernicus are present on which Solar System body?

a Venus   Mars **b**
c Pluto   The Moon **d**

16 Which planets have ring systems?

a All four giants   Saturn and Neptune **b**
c Saturn, Uranus, Jupiter   Saturn and Uranus **d**

17 The Oort Cloud contains an estimated 0.1–2 trillion…

a Rocky planets   Black holes **b**
c Galaxies   Icy bodies **d**

18 When was the European Space Agency (ESA) established?

a 1975   1980 **b**
c 1960   1970 **d**

19 GPS satellites were originally designed to last for how long?

a 5.5 years   7.5 years **b**
c 12.5 years   15.5 years **d**

20 After three billion years, the Milky Way may collide with which galaxy?

a Ursa Minor Dwarf   Bode's Galaxy **b**
c Cigar Galaxy   Andromeda Galaxy **d**

1 What surprising thing did astronomers find in the black hole of the Perseus galaxy cluster in 2003?

- **a** Alpha rays
- **b** Beta rays
- **c** Sound waves
- **d** Radio waves

2 Geocentric orbit refers to an orbit around which celestial body?

- **a** The Moon
- **b** The Sun
- **c** Mars
- **d** Earth

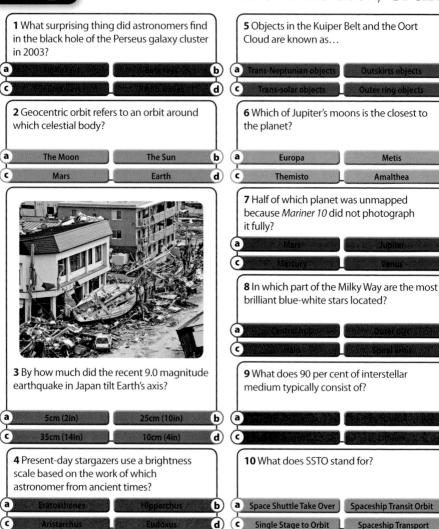

3 By how much did the recent 9.0 magnitude earthquake in Japan tilt Earth's axis?

- **a** 5cm (2in)
- **b** 25cm (10in)
- **c** 35cm (14in)
- **d** 10cm (4in)

4 Present-day stargazers use a brightness scale based on the work of which astronomer from ancient times?

- **a** Eratosthenes
- **b** Hipparchus
- **c** Aristarchus
- **d** Eudoxus

5 Objects in the Kuiper Belt and the Oort Cloud are known as…

- **a** Trans-Neptunian objects
- **b** Outskirts objects
- **c** Trans-solar objects
- **d** Outer ring objects

6 Which of Jupiter's moons is the closest to the planet?

- **a** Europa
- **b** Metis
- **c** Themisto
- **d** Amalthea

7 Half of which planet was unmapped because *Mariner 10* did not photograph it fully?

- **a** Mars
- **b** Jupiter
- **c** Mercury
- **d** Venus

8 In which part of the Milky Way are the most brilliant blue-white stars located?

- **a** Central hub
- **b** Outer disc
- **c** Halo
- **d** Spiral arms

9 What does 90 per cent of interstellar medium typically consist of?

- **a**
- **b** Dust
- **c**
- **d** Lithium

10 What does SSTO stand for?

- **a** Space Shuttle Take Over
- **b** Spaceship Transit Orbit
- **c** Single Stage to Orbit
- **d** Spaceship Transport

11 Which type of stars emit powerful beams of light, acting as natural lighthouses?

a Pulsars
b Brown Dwarf stars
c Carbon stars
d Wolf-Rayet stars

12 How long does it take the Hubble Space Telescope to complete a spin around Earth?

a 32 minutes
b 6 days
c 97 minutes
d 365 days

13 In total, how long did Neil Armstrong and Buzz Aldrin spend on the Moon's surface?

a 48 hours
b 21.5 hours
c 32 hours
d 15 hours

14 Which 2004 space mission brought back dust samples taken from the comet Wild 2?

a Cluster
b Cosmic Vision
c Rosetta
d Stardust

15 Which are the only two moons bigger than the planet Mercury?

a Ganymede and Titan
b Ganymede and Io
c Phobos and Deimos
d Miranda and Europa

16 The planet Venus is brightest during its…

a Full phase
b Solar transit
c Gibbous phase
d Crescent phase

17 Which NASA spacecraft was launched in 2006 to study Pluto?

a New Horizons
b MAVEN
c Expedition 30
d Nustar

18 On the television show *Sesame Street*, Ernie sang a bittersweet song entitled, "I Don't Want to Live…"

a Here
b In the Milky Way
c On the Moon
d Without Bert on Earth

19 Supermassive and stellar are types of…

a Galactic clusters
b Black holes
c Galaxies
d Constellations

20 Which star was known as the North Pole star in ancient times?

a
b
c Pollux
d Thuban

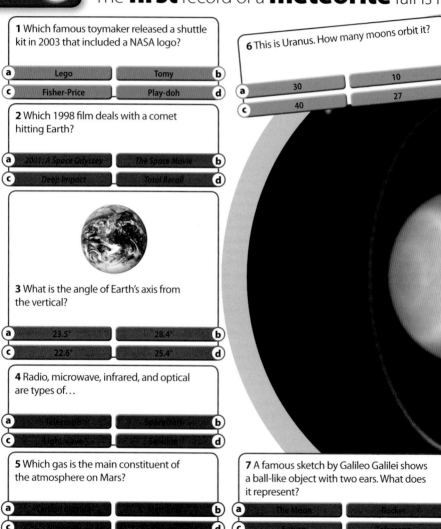

1 Which famous toymaker released a shuttle kit in 2003 that included a NASA logo?

a Lego
b Tomy
c Fisher-Price
d Play-doh

2 Which 1998 film deals with a comet hitting Earth?

a 2001: A Space Odyssey
b The Space Movie
c Deep Impact
d Total Recall

3 What is the angle of Earth's axis from the vertical?

a 23.5°
b 28.4°
c 22.6°
d 25.4°

4 Radio, microwave, infrared, and optical are types of…

a Telescope
b Spacecraft
c Light wave
d Satellite

5 Which gas is the main constituent of the atmosphere on Mars?

a Carbon dioxide
b Methane
c Nitrogen
d Helium

6 This is Uranus. How many moons orbit it?

a 30
10
c 40
27

7 A famous sketch by Galileo Galilei shows a ball-like object with two ears. What does it represent?

a The Moon
b Rocket
c Saturn
d Telescope

8 After the Sun and the Moon, which is the brightest object in Earth's sky?

a Sirius
b Mars
c Proxima Centauri
d Venus

9 Which planet has no geological activity or weather?

a Earth
b Mercury
c Mars
d Venus

10 In 1500, it took three years to sail around Earth. How far can a spaceship take you in three years?

a Beyond the Solar System
b To Saturn
c To the Moon
d To Mars

11 A collection of galaxies bound together by gravity is known as a…

a
b
c
d

12 Stony, iron, and stony-iron are all types of what?

a Dwarf planet
b Meteorite
c Asteroid
d Comet

13 Pluto was made a dwarf planet in 2006. Which is now the smallest planet in the Solar System?

a Earth
b Mars
c Mercury
d Venus

14 Which of these is not a zodiac constellation?

a
b
c
d

15 How do crew members of the International Space Station keep their muscles in shape in weightlessness?

a They eat a lot of red meat
b They float upside-down
c They go on spacewalks
d They use gym equipment

"**Astronaut**" comes from the **Greek**

1 Which planet is named after a Greek god who was the grandfather of Zeus?

- **a** Neptune
- **b** Saturn
- **c** Uranus
- **d** Jupiter

2 Comets with orbital periods of less than 200 years are known as…

- **a** Long-term comets
- **b** Momentary comets
- **c** Short-term comets
- **d** Periodic comets

3 Who first suggested that the Milky Way is a cluster of distant stars?

- **a** Democritus
- **b** Aristotle
- **c** Plato
- **d** Socrates

4 After the Sun, which is the star nearest to Earth?

- **a** Proxima Centauri
- **b** Procyon
- **c** Epsilon
- **d** Betelgeuse

5 Which is the largest solid body in the Solar System?

- **a** Venus
- **b** Mars
- **c** Pluto
- **d** Earth

6 Which galaxy consists of two galaxies colliding?

- **a** Andromeda
- **b** Pinwheel
- **c** Triangulum
- **d** Antennae

7 Which constellation, shown here, lies between Libra and Sagittarius?

- **a** Hercules
- **b** Crux
- **c** Scorpius
- **d** Cancer

8 Analysis of what has shown that Earth's outer core is liquid?

- **a** Tropical storms
- **b** Tornadoes
- **c** Earthquake waves
- **d** Tsunamis

9 In a solar eclipse, the period during which the Sun is completely hidden is called…

- **a** Totality
- **b** Obscurity
- **c** Ecliptic
- **d** Perigee

10 Which German astronomer first spotted Neptune, in 1846?

- **a** William Lassell
- **b** Johann Galle
- **c** Clyde Tombaugh
- **d** William Herschel

words for **star** and **sailor**

11 What do these craft have in common – *Pioneer 10* and *Pioneer 11*, *Voyager 1* and *Voyager 2*, and *Galileo*?

a They landed on the Moon
b They blew up on launch
c They explored Jupiter
d They failed

12 Which *Apollo* mission had to abort its Moon landing after an oxygen tank burst two days after its launch?

a Apollo 11
b Apollo 14
c Apollo 12
d Apollo 13

13 Which planet has distinctive coloured bands formed in its atmosphere?

a Jupiter
b Saturn
c Uranus
d Neptune

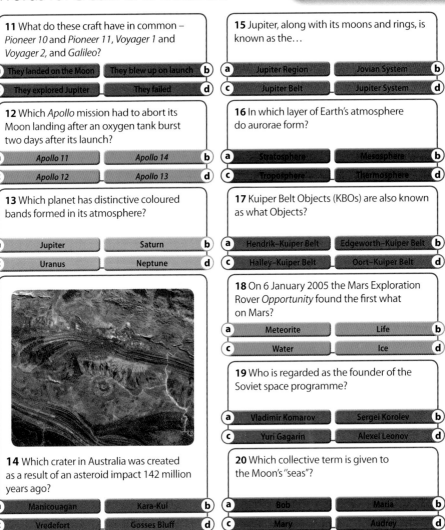

14 Which crater in Australia was created as a result of an asteroid impact 142 million years ago?

a Manicouagan
b Kara-Kul
c Vredefort
d Gosses Bluff

15 Jupiter, along with its moons and rings, is known as the…

a Jupiter Region
b Jovian System
c Jupiter Belt
d Jupiter System

16 In which layer of Earth's atmosphere do aurorae form?

a Stratosphere
b Mesosphere
c Troposphere
d Thermosphere

17 Kuiper Belt Objects (KBOs) are also known as what Objects?

a Hendrik–Kuiper Belt
b Edgeworth–Kuiper Belt
c Halley–Kuiper Belt
d Oort–Kuiper Belt

18 On 6 January 2005 the Mars Exploration Rover *Opportunity* found the first what on Mars?

a Meteorite
b Life
c Water
d Ice

19 Who is regarded as the founder of the Soviet space programme?

a Vladimir Komarov
b Sergei Korolev
c Yuri Gagarin
d Alexei Leonov

20 Which collective term is given to the Moon's "seas"?

a Bob
b Maria
c Mary
d Audrey

1 Which feature of a planet helps scientists measure its weight?

a Orbital period
b Gravitational pull
c Temperature
d Luminosity

2 The stars Sirius, Procyon, and Betelgeuse make up the…

a
b
c
d

3 Near-Earth asteroids with orbital periods of less than one year are called…

a Aten asteroids
b Amor asteroids
c Apollo asteroids
d Primary asteroids

4 Which of these men is Michael Collins, who orbited the moon as Neil Armstrong and Buzz Aldrin walked on it?

a
b
c
d

5 What are the two best known satellite galaxies of the Milky Way collectively called?

a
b
c
d

6 Who was the first woman to become the commander of a space shuttle?

a Eileen Collins
b Sally Ride
c Kathryn Sullivan
d Valentina Tereshkova

7 Which was the first European spacecraft to visit Venus?

a Venus Express
b Magellan
c Mariner
d Venera

8 Which spacecraft carried out a test for microbial life on Mars?

a Pioneers
b Vikings
c Voyagers
d Mariners

9 Which class of star does our Sun belong to at present?

a White dwarf
b Supernova
c Yellow dwarf
d Red giant

10 What is an unusually powerful supernova called?

a Meganova
b Hypernova
c
d Ultranova

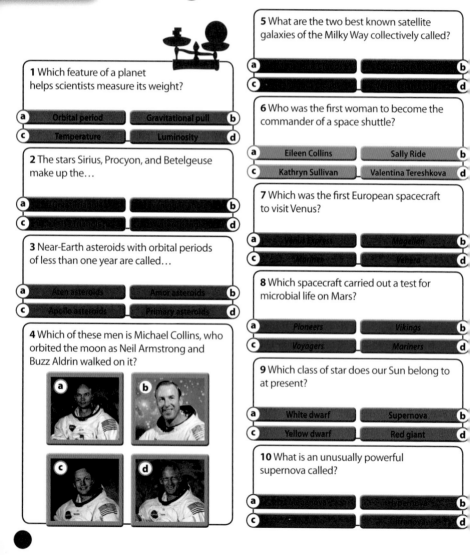

11 What are Venus's vast plains of volcanic lava called?

a Valles
b Chasms
c Regiones
d Planitiae

12 If you were in the northern hemisphere, which constellation would you not see in the night sky?

a Hydrus
b Ursa Major
c Ursa Minor
d Draco

13 If the "O" of SDO stands for Object, what does "SD" stand for?

a Small Dreaded
b Solar Diatomous
c Special Deteriorated
d Scattered Disk

14 Which ESA satellite, launched in 1989, measured the distances of millions of stars from Earth?

a Hubble
b Gaia
c SOHO
d Hipparcos

15 What is Uranus's atmosphere mainly made up of?

a Carbon dioxide
b Methane
c Hydrogen
d Helium

16 Where in the world is the biggest radio telescope dish located?

a Perth, Australia
b Arizona, US
c Santiago, Chile
d Arecibo, Puerto Rico

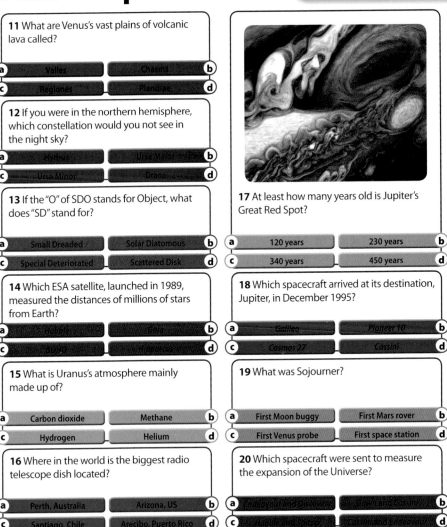

17 At least how many years old is Jupiter's Great Red Spot?

a 120 years
b 230 years
c 340 years
d 450 years

18 Which spacecraft arrived at its destination, Jupiter, in December 1995?

a Galileo
b Pioneer 10
c Cosmos 27
d Cassini

19 What was Sojourner?

a First Moon buggy
b First Mars rover
c First Venus probe
d First space station

20 Which spacecraft were sent to measure the expansion of the Universe?

a Endeavour and Discovery
b Dawn and Cassini
c Hubble and Spitzer
d Cassini and Endeavour

Black holes are black because the

1 *Sputnik 1* was the first artificial satellite to orbit Earth. It was launched in 1957 from where?

a China
b America
c Russia
d UK

2 In the original *Star Trek*, Captain Kirk led a crew on board the Starship…

a Comet
b Galaxy
c Universe
d Enterprise

3 What is a pattern of stars identifiable in the night sky called?

a
b
c
d

4 How long does it take Venus to make one complete spin on its axis?

a 125 days
b 243 days
c 179 days
d 96 days

5 When Earth, the Moon, and the Sun are lined up, what might we see?

a Explosion
b The Moon upside-down
c Eclipse
d End of the world

6 Which theory suggests that the Universe will ultimately be torn apart?

a
b
c
d

7 Which layer of Earth's atmosphere absorbs harmful ultraviolet rays?

a Ozone layer
b Mesosphere
c Thermosphere
d Troposphere

8 Which celestial body poses a threat to Earth in the film *Armageddon*?

a Meteorite
b Dwarf planet
c Asteroid
d Comet

light they suck in can't escape

9 In January 1959 the Soviet probe *Luna 1* became the first spacecraft to fly past what?

The Sun	The Moon **b**
Mars	Venus **d**

11 In 1969 David Bowie released which hit song that featured the fictional astronaut Major Tom?

a "Space Oddity"	"Looking for Space" **b**
c "Space Party"	"Ground Control" **d**

12 Which planet has the longest orbit around the Sun?

a Saturn	Jupiter **b**
c Uranus	Neptune **d**

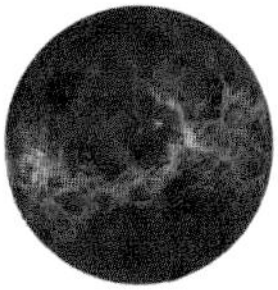

13 The orbital path of which planet (shown here) is least elliptical?

a Jupiter	Mars **b**
c Uranus	Venus **d**

14 Which is the third planet from the Sun?

a Earth	Venus **b**
c Mars	Jupiter **d**

10 Which is the brightest star in the night sky?

	b
	d

15 What is a fictional soldier of the imperial army in the *Star Wars* saga called?

a Yoda	Stormtrooper **b**
c Darth Vader	Buzz Lightyear **d**

1 Which Roman god of agriculture is one of the giant planets named after?

a) Jupiter
b) Neptune
c) Saturn
d) Mars

2 Which is the coldest planet in the Solar System?

a) Jupiter
b) Uranus
c) Neptune
d) Saturn

3 The enormous explosion that occurs when a supergiant star runs out of fuel is called a…

a)
b)
c)
d)

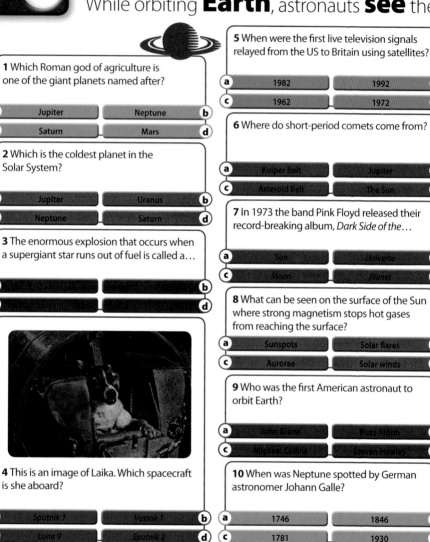

4 This is an image of Laika. Which spacecraft is she aboard?

a) Sputnik 1
b) Vostok 1
c) Luna 9
d) Sputnik 2

5 When were the first live television signals relayed from the US to Britain using satellites?

a) 1982
b) 1992
c) 1962
d) 1972

6 Where do short-period comets come from?

a) Kuiper Belt
b) Jupiter
c) Asteroid Belt
d) The Sun

7 In 1973 the band Pink Floyd released their record-breaking album, *Dark Side of the*…

a) Sun
b) Universe
c) Moon
d) Planet

8 What can be seen on the surface of the Sun where strong magnetism stops hot gases from reaching the surface?

a) Sunspots
b) Solar flares
c) Aurorae
d) Solar winds

9 Who was the first American astronaut to orbit Earth?

a) John Glenn
b) Buzz Aldrin
c) Michael Collins
d) Steven Hawley

10 When was Neptune spotted by German astronomer Johann Galle?

a) 1746
b) 1846
c) 1781
d) 1930

11 The most massive stars will eventually collapse to form…

a Black holes
b Dark matter
c Atoms
d Galaxies

12 Which was the last manned mission of the *Apollo* space programme?

a Apollo 20
b Apollo 17
c Apollo 11
d Apollo 15

13 Mars's moons, Phobos and Deimos, are named after the sons of which Greek god?

a Jupiter
b Zeus
c Atlas
d Ares

14 The constellation Lacerta represents which animal?

a
b
c
d

15 Which type of currents flow within Earth's mantle?

a Conduction
b Radiation
c Juicy
d Convection

16 What lies between the orbit of Neptune and the Oort Cloud?

a Asteroid Belt
b Black holes
c Comet Belt
d Kuiper Belt

17 What is the layer between the core and the convection zone of the Sun called?

a Exosphere
b Radiative zone
c Chromosphere
d Photosphere

18 Which star marks the tip of the tail of Ursa Minor, the Little Bear?

a Polaris
b Spica
c Rigel
d Aldabaran

19 What does LEO stand for?

a Low Earth Orbit
b Long External Orbit
c Largely Elevated Orbit
d Lagrangian Earth Orbit

20 Who launched the first liquid-fuelled rocket in 1926?

a Pedro Paulet
b Robert Goddard
c Wernher von Braun
d Sergei Korolev

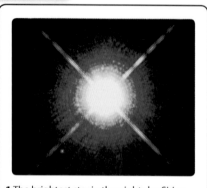

1 The brightest star in the night sky, Sirius, is in which constellation?

a		b	
c		d	

2 The Sun rotates faster at its equator than at its poles. What is happening?

a	Differential rotation	b	Separate rotation
c	Plasmodic rotation	d	Equatorial rotation

3 What type of system is STS?

a	Space Transportation	b	Space Tracking
c	Stellar Travelling	d	Secondary Transport

4 Only one side of the Moon faces Earth. What is this called?

a	Binary attraction	b	Magnetic lock
c	Binary pull	d	Tidal locking

5 Space technicians worked on *Huygens* at facilities in Bordeaux, France, in preparation for its journey to where?

a	Io		Titan
c	Jupiter		Ganymede

6 What does SNR stand for?

a			
c			

7 Earth-orbit-crossing asteroids with orbital periods of more than one year are called…

a	Apollo asteroids		Aten asteroids
c	Amor asteroids		Secondary asteroids

8 *Messenger* is orbiting Mercury. Which other spacecraft has visited Mercury?

a	Pioneer Venus 1		Magellan
c	Mariner 10		Venera

9 Which European satellite is on the lookout for exoplanets?

a	SOHO		COROT
c	Planck		XMM

10 Adams, Le Verrier, and Galle are associated with Neptune. What are they?

a	Craters		Rings
c	Cloud systems		Moons

11 Huge regions of space that have no galaxies are called…

Voids	Black holes	**b**
Dead space	Dark matter	**d**

12 What was Venus known as in Ancient Greece?

Romulus and Remus	Zeus and Apollo	**b**
Laurel and Hardy	Phosphorus and Hesperus	**d**

13 What is a star that is too small to sustain hydrogen nuclear fusion called?

Brown dwarf	Collapsar	**b**
Main sequence star	Neutron star	**d**

14 An asteroid in heliocentric orbit revolves around…

The Moon	Earth	**b**
A comet	The Sun	**d**

15 How many known natural planetary satellites are there in the Solar System?

98	168	**b**
176	137	**d**

16 Who proposed that stars are powered by nuclear fusion?

Annie Jump Cannon	Arthur Stanley Eddington	**b**
Hans Bethe	George Gamow	**d**

17 In a 1996 film starring Jack Nicholson, aliens from which planet are plotting to destroy humanity?

a	Neptune	Saturn	**b**
c	Mars	Jupiter	**d**

18 Which wavelength does the Spitzer Space Telescope observe in?

a	Ultraviolet	Radio	**b**
c	Infrared	X-ray	**d**

19 Which kind of stars dominate the neighbourhood of the Solar System?

a	Blue giants	Brown dwarfs	**b**
c	White dwarfs	Red dwarfs	**d**

20 Where on Mars did the rover *Spirit* land?

a	Ross Crater	Savannah Crater	**b**
c	Gusev Crater	Endurance Crater	**d**

1 Which is Saturn's largest moon?

- **a** Titan
- **b** Dione
- **c** Enceladus
- **d** Prometheus

2 Which of the following is not part of the Solar System?

- **a** Ceres
- **b** Titan
- **c** Asteroid Belt
- **d** Alpha Centauri

3 In space, which astronaut activity is known as Extra-Vehicular Activity?

- **a** Conducting experiments
- Spacewalking
- **c** Spacecraft repair
- Exercising

4 Earth's closest neighbour in space is…

- **a** Venus
- The Sun
- **c** The Moon
- Mars

5 *Salyut 1*, *Salyut 7*, *Mir*, and *Skylab* are names of…

- **a** Rockets
- Rovers
- **c** Space Institutes
- Space stations

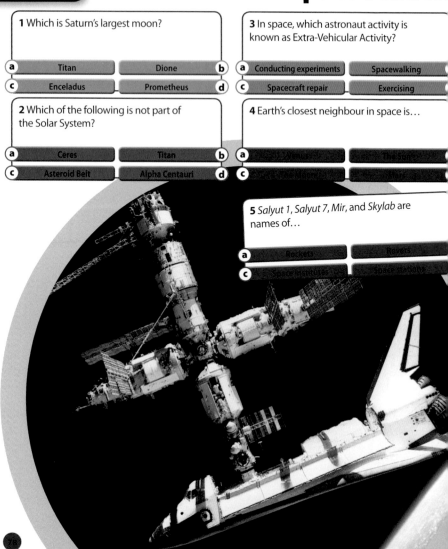

6 The constellation Orion depicts the figure of Orion, the mythological…

- a [illegible]
- b [illegible]
- c [illegible]
- d [illegible]

7 The knives and forks on board the International Space Station do not float away because they are…

- a Secured by magnets
- b Tied to the astronauts
- c Made of heavy metal
- d Not used in space

8 About how old is the Universe?

- a 13.7 billion years
- b 12 billion years
- c 10 billion years
- d 16 billion years

9 Which are the two main metals in Earth's core?

- a Copper and aluminium
- b Iron and nickel
- c Nickel and copper
- d Iron and aluminium

10 "In space no one can hear you scream" was the tag line for which cult science-fiction film?

- a *Deep Impact*
- b *Apollo 13*
- c *Alien*
- d *Lost in Space*

11 *Columbia*, *Discovery*, and *Endeavour* are all types of…

- a Space station
- b Space telescope
- c Space shuttle orbiter
- d Space rover

12 Which constellation is this?

- a [illegible]
- b [illegible]
- c [illegible]
- d [illegible]

13 How old is the Sun?

- a 5 billion years
- b 1 billion years
- c 13 billion years
- d 10 billion years

14 The Kuiper Belt is shaped like a…

- a Pizza slice
- b Muffin
- c Pancake
- d Doughnut

15 Who made the first scientific observation of the transit of Venus?

- a Galileo Galilei
- b Jeremiah Horrocks
- c Aristotle
- d Socrates

38

Dennis Tito, the first space **tourist**

1 For how many years after the Big Bang was the Universe an opaque fireball?

(a) 500,000 years
(b) 1,000,000 years
(c) 800,000 years
(d) 1,300,000 years

2 The only time you can see the corona of the Sun from Earth is during a…

(a) Total lunar eclipse
(b) Partial lunar eclipse
(c) Total solar eclipse
(d) Partial solar eclipse

3 Which spacecraft carried Lego figurines representing the Roman god Jupiter, his wife Juno, and Galileo Galilei?

(a) Juno
(b) Messenger
(c) Pioneer 10
(d) Cassini

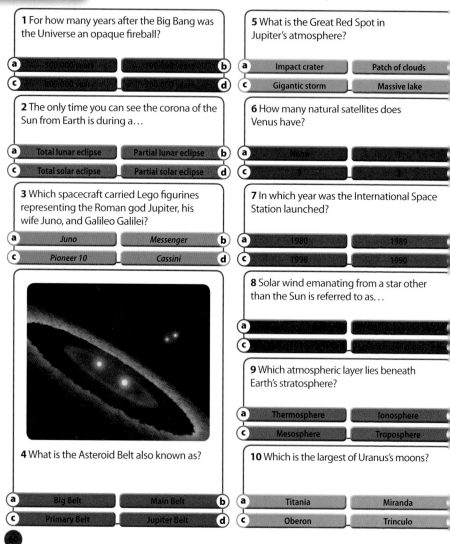

4 What is the Asteroid Belt also known as?

(a) Big Belt
(b) Main Belt
(c) Primary Belt
(d) Jupiter Belt

5 What is the Great Red Spot in Jupiter's atmosphere?

(a) Impact crater
(b) Patch of clouds
(c) Gigantic storm
(d) Massive lake

6 How many natural satellites does Venus have?

(a) None
(b) Two
(c) One
(d) Three

7 In which year was the International Space Station launched?

(a) 1980
(b) 1989
(c) 1998
(d) 1990

8 Solar wind emanating from a star other than the Sun is referred to as…

(a)
(b)
(c)
(d)

9 Which atmospheric layer lies beneath Earth's stratosphere?

(a) Thermosphere
(b) Ionosphere
(c) Mesosphere
(d) Troposphere

10 Which is the largest of Uranus's moons?

(a) Titania
(b) Miranda
(c) Oberon
(d) Trinculo

11 What are asteroids that come close to Earth called?

B-type asteroids	**b** A-type asteroids
Near-Earth asteroids	**d** Earthly asteroids

12 How far above Earth's surface does the Hubble Space Telescope orbit our planet?

60km (37 miles)	**b** 600km (373 miles)
6,000km (3,728 miles)	**d** 60,000km (37,282 miles)

13 Which rocky planet has the strongest magnetic field?

Mars	**b** Venus
Mercury	**d** Earth

14 Which is the fastest spinning planet in the Solar System?

Saturn	**b** Jupiter
Venus	**d** Uranus

15 Which is the only place in the Universe where natural nuclear fusion takes place?

	b
	d

16 Earth's magnetic field is shaped like…

A muffin	**b** An eclair
A doughnut	**d** A cookie

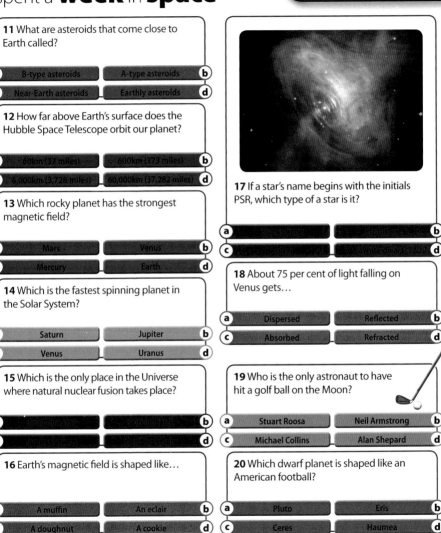

17 If a star's name begins with the initials PSR, which type of a star is it?

a	**b**
c	**d**

18 About 75 per cent of light falling on Venus gets…

a Dispersed	**b** Reflected
c Absorbed	**d** Refracted

19 Who is the only astronaut to have hit a golf ball on the Moon?

a Stuart Roosa	**b** Neil Armstrong
c Michael Collins	**d** Alan Shepard

20 Which dwarf planet is shaped like an American football?

a Pluto	**b** Eris
c Ceres	**d** Haumea

39

Saturn's rings are made

1 Which celestial objects are divided into classes indicated by the letters O, B, A, F, G, K, and M?

- **a** Planets
- **b** Galaxies
- **c** Nebulae
- **d** Stars

2 Which type of neutron star has an extremely strong magnetic field?

- **a** Protostar
- **b** Magnetar
- **c** White dwarf
- **d** O-class star

3 When two or more planets can be viewed in the same line of sight, what is the phenomenon called?

- **a** Opposition
- **b** Constellation
- **c** Happening
- **d** Conjunction

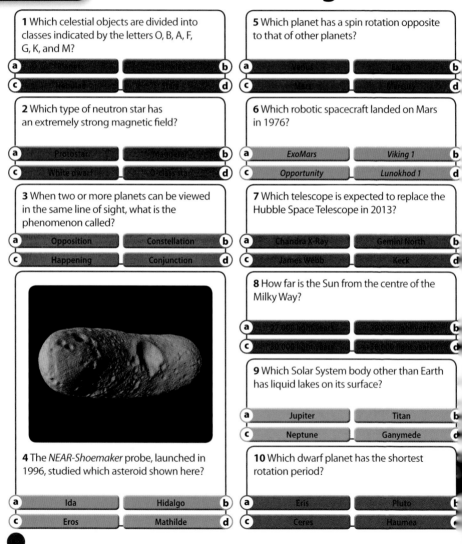

4 The *NEAR-Shoemaker* probe, launched in 1996, studied which asteroid shown here?

- **a** Ida
- **b** Hidalgo
- **c** Eros
- **d** Mathilde

5 Which planet has a spin rotation opposite to that of other planets?

- **a** Venus
- **b** Earth
- **c** Mars
- **d** Mercury

6 Which robotic spacecraft landed on Mars in 1976?

- **a** ExoMars
- **b** Viking 1
- **c** Opportunity
- **d** Lunokhod 1

7 Which telescope is expected to replace the Hubble Space Telescope in 2013?

- **a** Chandra X-Ray
- **b** Gemini North
- **c** James Webb
- **d** Keck

8 How far is the Sun from the centre of the Milky Way?

- **a** 27,000 light years
- **b** 20,000 light years
- **c** 30,000 light years
- **d** 36,000 light years

9 Which Solar System body other than Earth has liquid lakes on its surface?

- **a** Jupiter
- **b** Titan
- **c** Neptune
- **d** Ganymede

10 Which dwarf planet has the shortest rotation period?

- **a** Eris
- **b** Pluto
- **c** Ceres
- **d** Haumea

11 What do Jupiter's clouds probably smell like?

a Kerosene

b Rotten meat

c Rotten eggs, ammonia

d Sweaty socks

12 Pluto was discovered in 1930. Who discovered it?

a John Couch Adams

b Clyde Tombaugh

c William Herschel

d Alexis Bouvard

13 The findings of the *Wilkinson Microwave Anisotropy* probe revealed that the Universe…

a Will collapse

b Is expanding

c Is flat

d Is round

14 Observations of which space probe confirmed Venus's unusually slow rotation?

a Pioneer 6

b Mariner 2

c Pioneer 2

d Mariner 9

15 In a century, how many times does Mercury pass between Earth and the Sun?

a 43

b 22

c 13

d 74

16 How fast is the Andromeda Galaxy coming towards the Milky Way?

a 100kps (62mps)

b 800kps (497mps)

c 500kps (311mps)

d 300kps (186mps)

17 Which near-Earth asteroids approach but do not cross the orbit of Earth?

a Amor asteroids

b Apollo asteroids

c Aten asteroids

d Periodic asteroids

18 How many light years is the Merope Nebula from Earth?

a 440

b 340

c 500

d 100

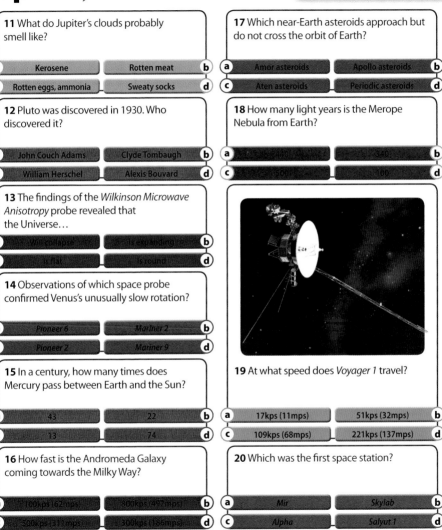

19 At what speed does *Voyager 1* travel?

a 17kps (11mps)

b 51kps (32mps)

c 109kps (68mps)

d 221kps (137mps)

20 Which was the first space station?

a Mir

b Skylab

c Alpha

d Salyut 1

At 77, **John Glenn** was the **oldest**

1 A scientist who studies space and celestial bodies is called an…

a Astrologist
b Anthropologist
c Archaeologist
d Astronomer

2 What did the *Lunar Prospector* spacecraft discover near the Moon's poles in 1999?

a Iron
b Silver
c Titanium
d Ice

3 Which type of galaxy is the Milky Way?

a Elliptical
b Barred spiral
c Spiral
d Irregular

4 Launched by the Soviet Union in 1971, *Salyut 1* was the world's first…

a Rocket
b Satellite to orbit Earth
c Mission to Mars
d Space station

5 Which planet is sometimes called the "red planet"?

a Jupiter
b Venus
c Mercury
d Mars

6 The star cluster Pleiades is also known as the…

a
b
c
d

7 Which planet has two moons, Phobos and Deimos?

a Uranus
b Mars
c Jupiter
d Venus

8 Name this English physicist who, despite physical disabilities, has made invaluable contributions to cosmology?

a Stephen Hawking
b
c
d

9 Roughly what percentage of Earth's surface is land?

a 40 per cent
b 35 per cent
c 30 per cent
d 25 per cent

10 Which was the first shuttle orbiter to launch into space?

a Endeavour
b Discovery
c Columbia
d Atlantis

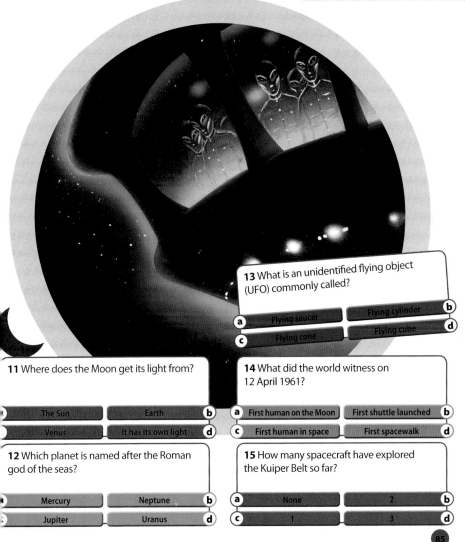

13 What is an unidentified flying object (UFO) commonly called?

a Flying saucer
b Flying cylinder
c Flying cone
d Flying cube

11 Where does the Moon get its light from?

The Sun
b Earth
Venus
d It has its own light

12 Which planet is named after the Roman god of the seas?

Mercury
b Neptune
Jupiter
d Uranus

14 What did the world witness on 12 April 1961?

a First human on the Moon
b First shuttle launched
c First human in space
d First spacewalk

15 How many spacecraft have explored the Kuiper Belt so far?

a None
b 2
c 1
d 3

A **star's mass** determines how

1 Which of these planets can never experience a solar eclipse?

a Mars
b Venus
c Earth
d Jupiter

2 Who wrote the lyrics of the English nursery rhyme "Twinkle, twinkle, little star"?

a James Joyce
b William Blake
c Jane Taylor
d Robert Browning

3 Which planet's atmospheric pressure is 90 times greater than that at Earth's surface?

a Venus
b Mercury
c Neptune
d Mars

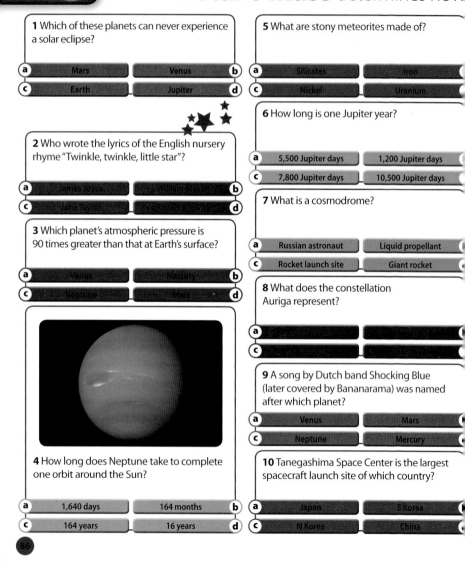

4 How long does Neptune take to complete one orbit around the Sun?

a 1,640 days
b 164 months
c 164 years
d 16 years

5 What are stony meteorites made of?

a Silicates
b Iron
c Nickel
d Uranium

6 How long is one Jupiter year?

a 5,500 Jupiter days
b 1,200 Jupiter days
c 7,800 Jupiter days
d 10,500 Jupiter days

7 What is a cosmodrome?

a Russian astronaut
b Liquid propellant
c Rocket launch site
d Giant rocket

8 What does the constellation Auriga represent?

a
c

9 A song by Dutch band Shocking Blue (later covered by Bananarama) was named after which planet?

a Venus
b Mars
c Neptune
d Mercury

10 Tanegashima Space Center is the largest spacecraft launch site of which country?

a Japan
b S Korea
c N Korea
d China

long it is going to **live**

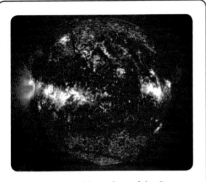

11 What is the visible surface of the Sun, pictured here, called?

a Penumbra | Photosphere b
c Corona | Chromosphere d

12 When did the International Astronomical Union coin the term "dwarf planet"?

a 2004 | 2000 b
c 2010 | 2006 d

13 What is the long-duration mission to the International Space Station that was launched in 2011 called?

a Expedition 2000 | Expedition 2011 b
c Expedition 30 | Expedition 29 d

14 Which was the first remote-controlled rover to land on another celestial body?

a Lunar Roving Vehicle | Lunokhod 1 b
c Spirit | Curiosity d

15 In which year did the *Challenger* disaster, which led to the deaths of its seven crew members, occur?

a 1980 | 1986 b
c 1984 | 1989 d

16 Which planet has the most volcanic moon in the Solar System?

a Venus | Jupiter b
c Mars | Earth d

17 How many moons orbit Mars?

a 2 | 3 b
c 1 | 5 d

18 An abundance of which element was found on Jupiter's moon Io?

a Lead | Iron b
c Nickel | Sulphur d

19 How long after the Big Bang are the first stars believed to have formed?

a 50 million years | 200 million years b
c 350 million years | 500 million years d

20 Which of the following moons is not spherical?

a Ganymede | Rhea b
c Phobos | Titan d

Comets are made of material unchanged

1 Which planet has a magnetic field about 100 times weaker than Earth's?

- **a** Venus
- **b** Mars
- **c** Saturn
- **d** Mercury

2 Which astrophysicist first coined the word supernova?

- **a** Fritz Zwicky
- **b** Stephen Hawking
- **c** Johannes Kepler
- **d** Harlow Shapley

3 The Sikhote-Alin meteorite fell on Earth in 1947. Where did it fall?

- **a** Siberia
- **b** Pacific Ocean
- **c** Alaska, US
- **d** Philippines

4 What is the diameter of the Orion Nebula?

- **a** 2 light years
- **b** 4 light years
- **c** 2.4 light years
- **d** 24 light years

5 The nebular hypothesis – the idea that the Solar System formed from a cloud of gas and dust – was proposed by…

- **a** Immanuel Kant
- **b** Isaac Newton
- **c** Joseph Louis Lagrange
- **d** Laura Bassi

6 Which space telescope is used by scientists to study black holes and exploding stars?

- **a** Herschel
- **b** Chandra
- **c** Hubble
- **d** Spitzer

7 When was the first solar-flare-induced quake in the Sun recorded?

- **a** 2000
- **b** 1996
- **c** 1993
- **d** 1998

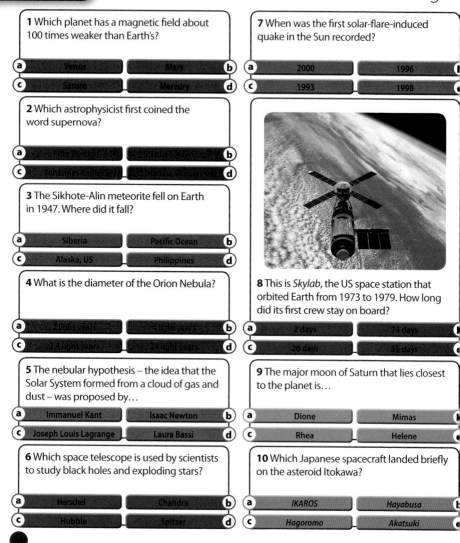

8 This is *Skylab*, the US space station that orbited Earth from 1973 to 1979. How long did its first crew stay on board?

- **a** 2 days
- **b** 74 days
- **c** 26 days
- **d** 35 days

9 The major moon of Saturn that lies closest to the planet is…

- **a** Dione
- **b** Mimas
- **c** Rhea
- **d** Helene

10 Which Japanese spacecraft landed briefly on the asteroid Itokawa?

- **a** IKAROS
- **b** Hayabusa
- **c** Hagoromo
- **d** Akatsuki

11 What is the unit for measuring declination?

a
b
c
d

12 Along with Robert Wilson, who discovered cosmic background radiation in the 1960s?

a Samuel Ting
b David Gross
c Arno Penzias
d William Phillips

13 Which trans-Neptunian object has a 10,500-year-long orbit?

a Makemake
b Teharonhiawako
c Sedna
d Haumea

14 Who wrote the science-fiction comedy series *The Hitchhiker's Guide to the Galaxy*?

a Arthur C Clarke
b Isaac Asimov
c Neil Gaiman
d Douglas Adams

15 On Mercury, how many Earth days are there between one sunrise and the next?

a 348
b 110
c 176
d 156

16 About how many times bigger is the Sun than the Moon?

a 600
b 800
c 400
d 200

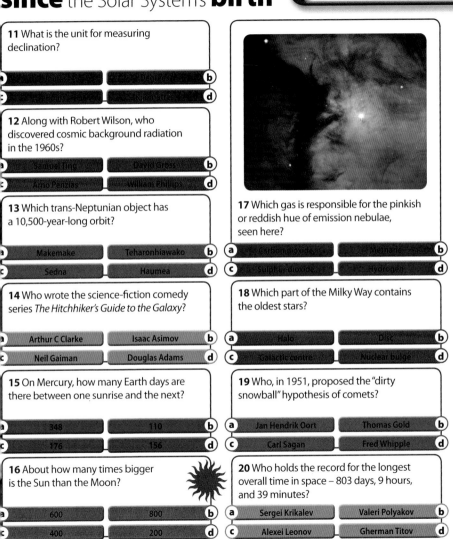

17 Which gas is responsible for the pinkish or reddish hue of emission nebulae, seen here?

a Carbon dioxide
b Methane
c Sulphur dioxide
d Hydrogen

18 Which part of the Milky Way contains the oldest stars?

a Halo
b Disc
c Galactic centre
d Nuclear bulge

19 Who, in 1951, proposed the "dirty snowball" hypothesis of comets?

a Jan Hendrik Oort
b Thomas Gold
c Carl Sagan
d Fred Whipple

20 Who holds the record for the longest overall time in space – 803 days, 9 hours, and 39 minutes?

a Sergei Krikalev
b Valeri Polyakov
c Alexei Leonov
d Gherman Titov

Cosmonaut **Sergei Krikalev** has spent

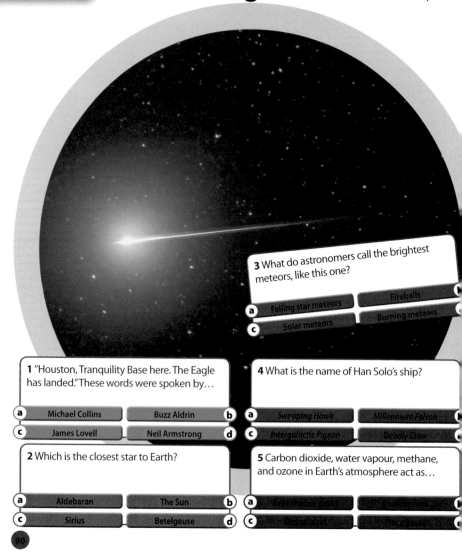

3 What do astronomers call the brightest meteors, like this one?

a. Falling star meteors

Fireballs

c. Solar meteors

Burning meteors

1 "Houston, Tranquility Base here. The Eagle has landed." These words were spoken by…

a. Michael Collins

b. Buzz Aldrin

c. James Lovell

d. Neil Armstrong

2 Which is the closest star to Earth?

a. Aldebaran

b. The Sun

c. Sirius

d. Betelgeuse

4 What is the name of Han Solo's ship?

a. Swooping Hawk

Millennium Falcon

c. Intergalactic Pigeon

Deadly Crow

5 Carbon dioxide, water vapour, methane, and ozone in Earth's atmosphere act as…

a. Greenhouse gases

Stratosphere

c. Ozone layer

Toxic gases

6 Which galaxy are we in?

a Black Eye Galaxy   Andromeda Galaxy **b**

c Milky Way Galaxy   Whirlpool Galaxy **d**

7 The Sun passes through which constellation between 19 January and 16 February?

a Capricorn   Aquarius **b**

c Sagittarius   Libra **d**

8 According to folklore, which lunar phase triggers a human's transformation into a werewolf?

a First quarter   Waning crescent **b**

c Full Moon   New Moon **d**

9 Which instrument is used by scientists to observe distant objects in space?

a Stethoscope   Telescope **b**

c Periscope   Microscope **d**

10 Which is the hottest layer of Earth's atmosphere?

a Stratosphere   Mesosphere **b**

c Troposphere   Thermosphere **d**

11 Where is the huge storm known as the Great Red Spot located?

a Venus   Neptune **b**

c Jupiter   Mars **d**

12 When did Galileo Galilei first use a telescope?

a 1609   1509 **b**

c 1709   1809 **d**

13 What happened on 21 July 1969?

a First human in space   First human on the Moon **b**

c Discovery of Pluto   Invention of the telescope **d**

14 How long is the orbital period of Halley's Comet?

a 76 years   128 years **b**

c 86 years   210 years **d**

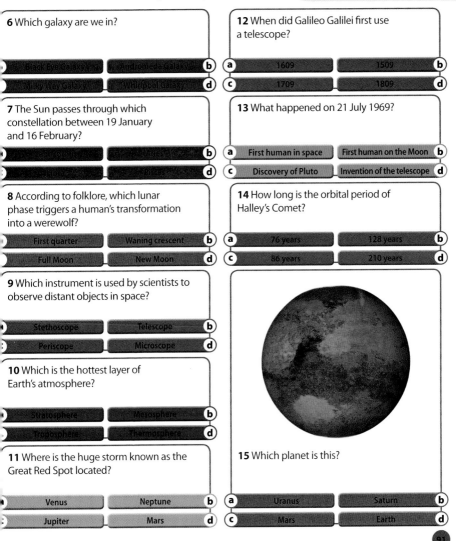

15 Which planet is this?

a Uranus   Saturn **b**

c Mars   Earth **d**

1 Which planet looks like a pale blue disc?

| a | Mercury | Pluto | b |
| c | Uranus | Venus | d |

2 How thick can Earth's oceanic crust be?

| a | 113km (70 miles) | 7m (23ft) | b |
| c | 2m (7ft) | 11km (7 miles) | d |

3 The Leonid meteor shower is said to originate in which constellation?

| a | | | b |
| c | | | d |

4 Which planet takes longer to complete one spin on its axis than it does to orbit once around the Sun?

| a | Venus | Mars | b |
| c | Neptune | Pluto | d |

5 What does the word "comet" mean?

| a | Shooting star | Long-tailed star | b |
| c | Dust star | Long-haired star | d |

6 How old is the Milky Way Galaxy?

| a | 13.2 billion years | 132 billion years | b |
| c | 1.32 billion years | 132 million years | d |

7 How much taller do people grow when they are in space, because of the lack of gravity?

| a | About 5cm (2in) | About 12cm (5in) | |
| c | About 1cm (⅖in) | About 20cm (8in) | |

8 Which is the largest space-themed park in the world?

| a | Disneyland, Paris | Cosmosphere, Hutchison | |
| c | Space City, Toulouse | Alien World, London | |

9 The sinking of Earth's crust into the mantle is called…

| a | Convection | Radiation | |
| c | Subduction | Conduction | |

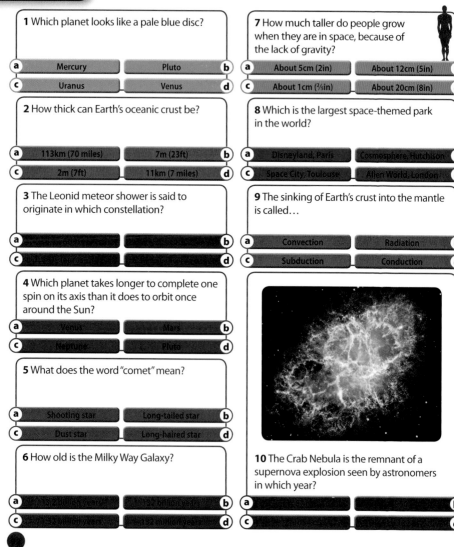

10 The Crab Nebula is the remnant of a supernova explosion seen by astronomers in which year?

| a | | | |
| c | | | |

11 The moon Larissa orbits which planet?

Uranus	Saturn (b)
Jupiter	Neptune (d)

12 Which satellite of Saturn reflects almost all of the sunlight it receives?

Hyperion	Enceladus (b)
Mimas	Titan (d)

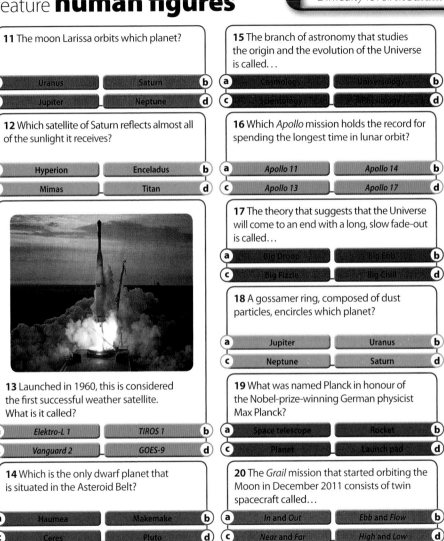

13 Launched in 1960, this is considered the first successful weather satellite. What is it called?

Elektro-L 1	TIROS 1 (b)
Vanguard 2	GOES-9 (d)

14 Which is the only dwarf planet that is situated in the Asteroid Belt?

Haumea	Makemake (b)
Ceres	Pluto (d)

15 The branch of astronomy that studies the origin and the evolution of the Universe is called...

(a) Cosmology	Universology (b)
(c) Scientology	Physiology (d)

16 Which *Apollo* mission holds the record for spending the longest time in lunar orbit?

(a) Apollo 11	Apollo 14 (b)
(c) Apollo 13	Apollo 17 (d)

17 The theory that suggests that the Universe will come to an end with a long, slow fade-out is called...

(a) Big Droop	Big Ebb (b)
(c) Big Fizzle	Big Chill (d)

18 A gossamer ring, composed of dust particles, encircles which planet?

(a) Jupiter	Uranus (b)
(c) Neptune	Saturn (d)

19 What was named Planck in honour of the Nobel-prize-winning German physicist Max Planck?

(a) Space telescope	Rocket (b)
(c) Planet	Launch pad (d)

20 The *Grail* mission that started orbiting the Moon in December 2011 consists of twin spacecraft called...

(a) In and Out	Ebb and Flow (b)
(c) Near and Far	High and Low (d)

1 Approximately how many tonnes of meteorites enter Earth's atmosphere each day?

a | 125
b | 200
c | 225
d | 100

2 Valles Marineris, a huge and complex system of canyons, is found on which planet?

a | Mars
b | Mercury
c | Earth
d | Venus

3 The spacecraft *Galileo* was launched in 1989 to study Jupiter. How many years did it take to reach its destination?

a | 1
b | 6
c | 12
d | 10

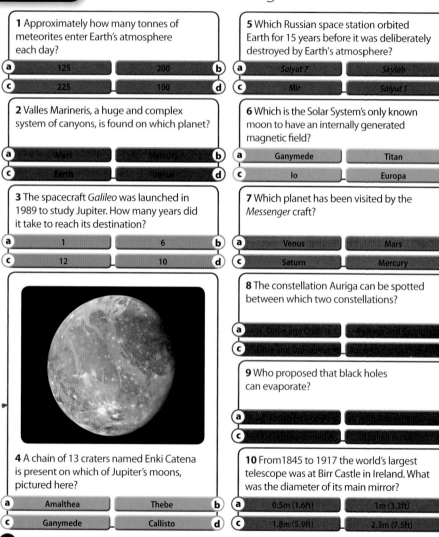

4 A chain of 13 craters named Enki Catena is present on which of Jupiter's moons, pictured here?

a | Amalthea
b | Thebe
c | Ganymede
d | Callisto

5 Which Russian space station orbited Earth for 15 years before it was deliberately destroyed by Earth's atmosphere?

a | *Salyut 7*
b | *Skylab*
c | *Mir*
d | *Salyut 1*

6 Which is the Solar System's only known moon to have an internally generated magnetic field?

a | Ganymede
b | Titan
c | Io
d | Europa

7 Which planet has been visited by the *Messenger* craft?

a | Venus
b | Mars
c | Saturn
d | Mercury

8 The constellation Auriga can be spotted between which two constellations?

a | Orion and Crux
b | Perseus and Gemini
c | Libra and Ophiuchus
d | Aquila and the Southern Cross

9 Who proposed that black holes can evaporate?

a | Stephen Hawking
b | Roger Penrose
c | Karl Schwarzschild
d | John Wheeler

10 From 1845 to 1917 the world's largest telescope was at Birr Castle in Ireland. What was the diameter of its main mirror?

a | 0.5m (1.6ft)
b | 1m (3.3ft)
c | 1.8m (5.9ft)
d | 2.3m (7.5ft)

11 Which was the first spacecraft to make a controlled, or soft, landing on the Moon?

| Luna 9 | Apollo 11 | **b** |
| Surveyor 3 | Ranger 1 | **d** |

12 Which is the biggest and brightest star cluster visible in the sky?

| | | **b** |
| | Omega Centauri | **d** |

13 The atmosphere of Saturn's moon Titan is primarily made up of…

| Argon | Nitrogen | **b** |
| Hydrogen | Helium | **d** |

14 The heaviest object ever launched into space was the…

| Luna spacecraft | Skylab space station | **b** |
| Ariel satellite | Salyut space station | **d** |

15 What is the typical diameter of a crater produced when a 1km (0.6-mile) asteroid hits one of Earth's continents?

| 12km (7 miles) | 17km (11 miles) | **b** |
| 7km (4 miles) | 23km (14 miles) | **d** |

16 The volcanoes Sif Mons and Gula Mons can be found on…

| The Moon | Titan | **b** |
| Venus | Mars | **d** |

17 Approximately how many times a day does the International Space Station orbit Earth?

| **a** | 25 | 2 | **b** |
| **c** | 7 | 16 | **d** |

18 What is the average distance between the stars in the vicinity of the Sun?

| **a** | 2 light years | 4 light years | **b** |
| **c** | 10 light years | 8 light years | **d** |

19 Which of the following is an example of a binary star system?

| **a** | | | **b** |
| **c** | | | **d** |

20 Lagoon, Hourglass, Cat's Eye, and Butterfly are names inspired by shapes. What are they the names of?

| **a** | Galactic clusters | Constellations | **b** |
| **c** | Nebulae | Galaxies | **d** |

More than 30,000 **meteorites** have

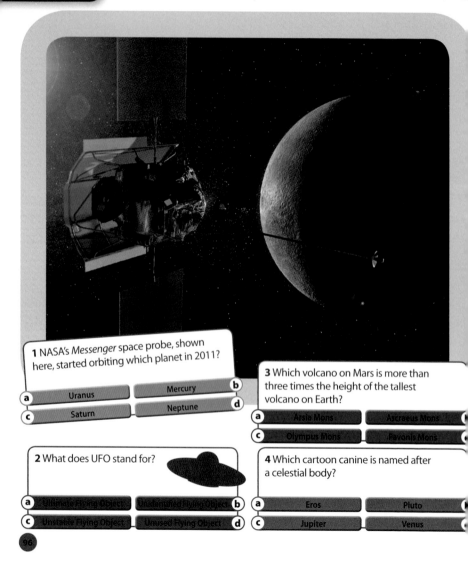

1 NASA's *Messenger* space probe, shown here, started orbiting which planet in 2011?

a Uranus
b Mercury
c Saturn
d Neptune

2 What does UFO stand for?

a Ultimate Flying Object
b Unidentified Flying Object
c Unstable Flying Object
d Unused Flying Object

3 Which volcano on Mars is more than three times the height of the tallest volcano on Earth?

a Arsia Mons
Ascraeus Mons
c Olympus Mons
Pavonis Mons

4 Which cartoon canine is named after a celestial body?

a Eros
Pluto
c Jupiter
Venus

5 Stephen Hawking is the author of which of these books?

a The First Three Minutes
b Black Holes and Time Warps
c A Brief History of Time
d The Origin of the Universe

6 All weather phenomena on Earth occur in its atmosphere's lowest layer. What is this layer called?

a Mesosphere
b Troposphere
c Ionosphere
d Stratosphere

7 Which planets are on either side of the Asteroid Belt?

a Earth and Mars
b Jupiter and Saturn
c Saturn and Uranus
d Mars and Jupiter

8 An asteroid hit Earth about 65 million years ago. What is thought to have happened?

a Ice age ended
b Himalayas formed
c Dinosaurs died out
d First humans appeared

9 What is at the centre of the Milky Way Galaxy?

a Quasar
b Worm hole
c Globular cluster
d Black hole

10 Who was the first woman in space?

a Valentina Tereshkova
b Sally Ride
c Helen Sharman
d Susan Helms

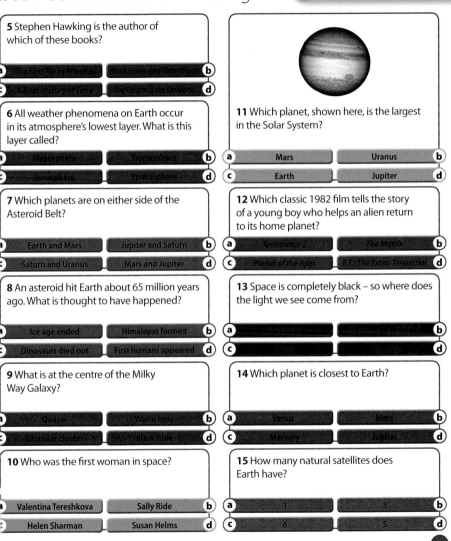

11 Which planet, shown here, is the largest in the Solar System?

a Mars
b Uranus
c Earth
d Jupiter

12 Which classic 1982 film tells the story of a young boy who helps an alien return to its home planet?

a Terminator 2
b The Matrix
c Planet of the Apes
d E.T.: The Extra-Terrestrial

13 Space is completely black – so where does the light we see come from?

a
b
c
d

14 Which planet is closest to Earth?

a Venus
b Mars
c Mercury
d Jupiter

15 How many natural satellites does Earth have?

a 1
b 3
c 6
d 5

The **biggest** constellation is **Hydra**,

1 ESA's *Rosetta* spacecraft will arrive at Comet Churyumov-Gerasimenko in 2014, and release which lander?

a. Nile
b. Stone
c. Obelisk
d. Philae

2 Which stellar pattern do the three stars Altair, Vega, and Deneb form?

a.
b.
c. Three Blind Mice
d. Summer Triangle

3 In which year was the dwarf planet Ceres discovered?

a. 1952
b. 2000
c. 2006
d. 1801

4 Which type of galaxy is the Andromeda Galaxy?

a. Spiral
b. Elliptical
c. Irregular
d. Lenticular

5 The brief glow of a meteor in Earth's sky is known as a…

a. Wake
b. Trail
c. Afterglow
d. Flash

6 Which was the first spacecraft to land on the surface of the Moon?

a. Ranger 1
b. Surveyor 1
c. Luna 2
d. Lunokhod 1

7 American astronaut Theodore Freeman was killed when his T-38 jet collided with a…

a. Mountain
b. Helicopter
c. Building
d. Goose

8 Since when has *Venus Express* been investigating the atmosphere of Venus?

a. 2006
b. 2004
c. 2009
d. 2007

9 What is the name of the largest moon in the Solar System?

a. Ganymede
b. Io
c. Galifrey
d. Titan

10 Which kind of telescope is this?

a. Radio
b. Microwave
c. Infrared
d. Optical

11 What is Saturn's atmosphere mostly made up of?

- Sulphur and hydrogen
- **b** Nitrogen and methane
- Hydrogen and helium
- **d** Hydrogen and nitrogen

12 Which is the only spacecraft to have travelled more than 17.7 billion km (11 billion miles) from the Sun?

- Cassini
- **b** Voyager 1
- Voyager 2
- **d** Magellan

13 The Moon does not have…

- **a** A mantle
- **b** A core
- **c** An atmosphere
- **d** A crust

14 What is at the core of the four giant planets?

- **a** Lava
- **b** Rock and ice
- **c** Iron
- **d** Gas

15 Hubble Deep Field, an image of the sky taken by the Hubble Space Telescope in 1995, revealed thousands of…

- **a** Black holes
- **b** Quasars
- **c** Nebulae
- **d** Galaxies

16 If you could find an ocean large enough to put all the planets in it, which planet would float?

- **a** Jupiter
- **b** Saturn
- **c** Mercury
- **d** None

17 Japan's Subaru Telescope is named after a star cluster known in English as…

- **a** Hyades
- **b** Trapezium
- **c** Pleiades
- **d** Christmas Tree

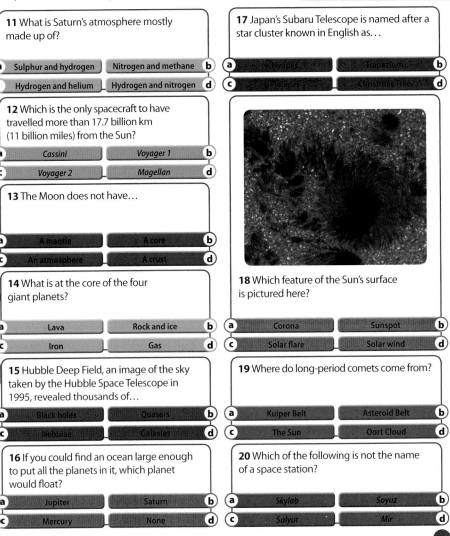

18 Which feature of the Sun's surface is pictured here?

- **a** Corona
- **b** Sunspot
- **c** Solar flare
- **d** Solar wind

19 Where do long-period comets come from?

- **a** Kuiper Belt
- **b** Asteroid Belt
- **c** The Sun
- **d** Oort Cloud

20 Which of the following is not the name of a space station?

- **a** Skylab
- **b** Soyuz
- **c** Salyut
- **d** Mir

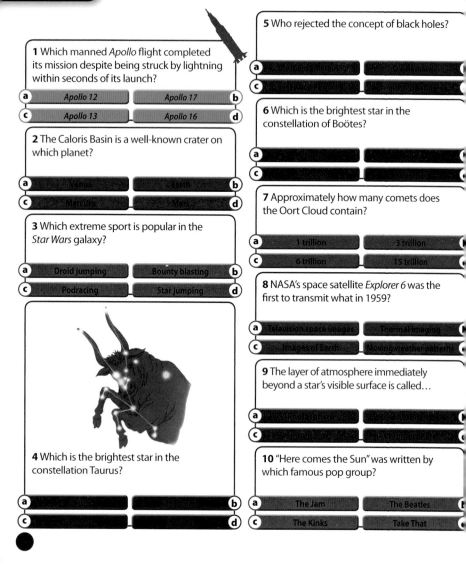

1 Which manned *Apollo* flight completed its mission despite being struck by lightning within seconds of its launch?

a Apollo 12
b Apollo 17
c Apollo 13
d Apollo 16

2 The Caloris Basin is a well-known crater on which planet?

a Venus
b Earth
c Mercury
d Mars

3 Which extreme sport is popular in the *Star Wars* galaxy?

a Droid jumping
b Bounty blasting
c Podracing
d Star jumping

4 Which is the brightest star in the constellation Taurus?

a
b
c
d

5 Who rejected the concept of black holes?

a
c

6 Which is the brightest star in the constellation of Boötes?

a
c

7 Approximately how many comets does the Oort Cloud contain?

a 1 trillion
3 trillion
c 6 trillion
15 trillion

8 NASA's space satellite *Explorer 6* was the first to transmit what in 1959?

a Television space images
Thermal imaging
c Images of Earth
Moving weather patterns

9 The layer of atmosphere immediately beyond a star's visible surface is called…

a Photosphere
c

10 "Here comes the Sun" was written by which famous pop group?

a The Jam
b The Beatles
c The Kinks
Take That

11 The largest crater on Venus is known as…

a Copernicus | b Yuty
c King | d Mead

12 What was found on the lunar rock collected during the *Apollo 17* mission?

a Diamonds | b Orange glass
c Sapphires | d Marble

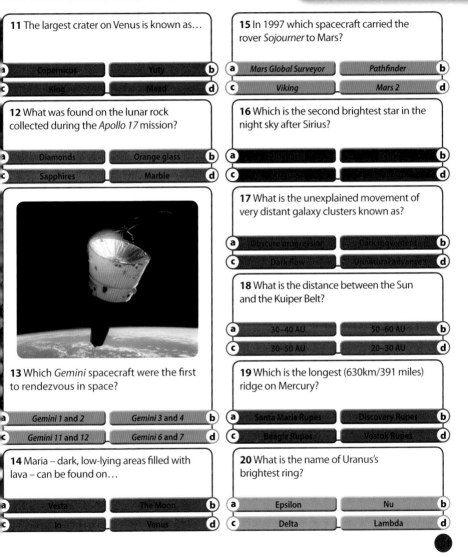

13 Which *Gemini* spacecraft were the first to rendezvous in space?

a Gemini 1 and 2 | b Gemini 3 and 4
c Gemini 11 and 12 | d Gemini 6 and 7

14 Maria – dark, low-lying areas filled with lava – can be found on…

a Vesta | b The Moon
c Io | d Venus

15 In 1997 which spacecraft carried the rover *Sojourner* to Mars?

a Mars Global Surveyor | b Pathfinder
c Viking | d Mars 2

16 Which is the second brightest star in the night sky after Sirius?

a | b
c | d

17 What is the unexplained movement of very distant galaxy clusters known as?

a Obscure progression | b Dark movement
c Dark flow | d Unnatural advance

18 What is the distance between the Sun and the Kuiper Belt?

a 30–40 AU | b 50–60 AU
c 30–50 AU | d 20–30 AU

19 Which is the longest (630km/391 miles) ridge on Mercury?

a Santa Maria Rupes | b Discovery Rupes
c Beagle Rupes | d Vostok Rupes

20 What is the name of Uranus's brightest ring?

a Epsilon | b Nu
c Delta | d Lambda

A **spacecraft** takes about 60 hours to

1 In the film *Apollo 13*, which actor played the role of Jim Lovell, the commander of the unsuccessful mission?

a Jack Nicholson
b Tom Cruise
c Tom Hanks
d Morgan Freeman

2 What is the name of Gustav Holst's space-themed musical suite?

a Jupiter
b Mars, the Bringer of War
c Shooting stars
d The Planets

3 Often found on the tops of high mountains, major observatories are also sometimes located on…

a Islands
b Rocky plains
c Extinct volcanoes
d Seaports

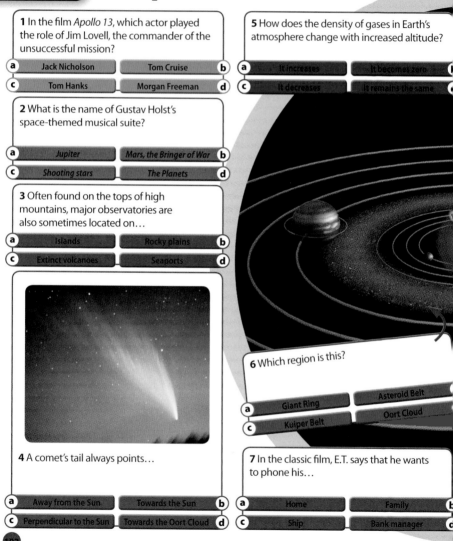

4 A comet's tail always points…

a Away from the Sun
b Towards the Sun
c Perpendicular to the Sun
d Towards the Oort Cloud

5 How does the density of gases in Earth's atmosphere change with increased altitude?

a It increases
b It becomes zero
c It decreases
d It remains the same

6 Which region is this?

a Giant Ring
b Asteroid Belt
c Kuiper Belt
d Oort Cloud

7 In the classic film, E.T. says that he wants to phone his…

a Home
b Family
c Ship
d Bank manager

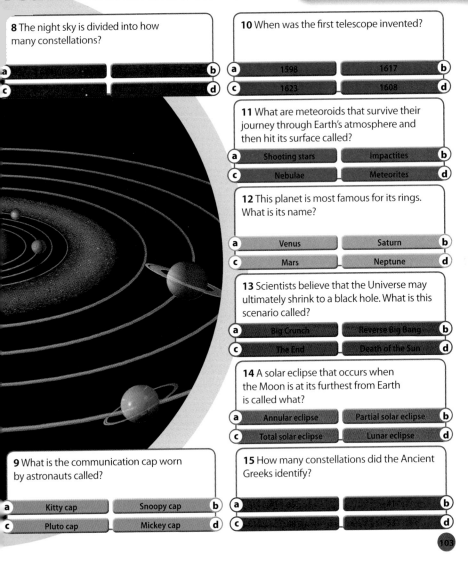

8 The night sky is divided into how many constellations?

(a)
(b)
(c)
(d)

9 What is the communication cap worn by astronauts called?

(a) Kitty cap
(b) Snoopy cap
(c) Pluto cap
(d) Mickey cap

10 When was the first telescope invented?

(a) 1598
(b) 1617
(c) 1623
(d) 1608

11 What are meteoroids that survive their journey through Earth's atmosphere and then hit its surface called?

(a) Shooting stars
(b) Impactites
(c) Nebulae
(d) Meteorites

12 This planet is most famous for its rings. What is its name?

(a) Venus
(b) Saturn
(c) Mars
(d) Neptune

13 Scientists believe that the Universe may ultimately shrink to a black hole. What is this scenario called?

(a) Big Crunch
(b) Reverse Big Bang
(c) The End
(d) Death of the Sun

14 A solar eclipse that occurs when the Moon is at its furthest from Earth is called what?

(a) Annular eclipse
(b) Partial solar eclipse
(c) Total solar eclipse
(d) Lunar eclipse

15 How many constellations did the Ancient Greeks identify?

(a)
(b)
(c)
(d)

An **asterism** is a star pattern that forms

1 Which is the only space probe to have visited four planets?

- (a)
- (b)
- (c)
- (d)

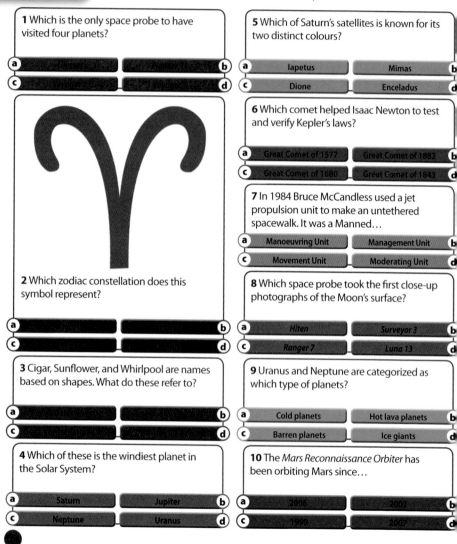

2 Which zodiac constellation does this symbol represent?

- (a)
- (b)
- (c)
- (d)

3 Cigar, Sunflower, and Whirlpool are names based on shapes. What do these refer to?

- (a)
- (b)
- (c)
- (d)

4 Which of these is the windiest planet in the Solar System?

- (a) Saturn
- (b) Jupiter
- (c) Neptune
- (d) Uranus

5 Which of Saturn's satellites is known for its two distinct colours?

- (a) Iapetus
- (b) Mimas
- (c) Dione
- (d) Enceladus

6 Which comet helped Isaac Newton to test and verify Kepler's laws?

- (a) Great Comet of 1577
- (b) Great Comet of 1882
- (c) Great Comet of 1680
- (d) Great Comet of 1843

7 In 1984 Bruce McCandless used a jet propulsion unit to make an untethered spacewalk. It was a Manned…

- (a) Manoeuvring Unit
- (b) Management Unit
- (c) Movement Unit
- (d) Moderating Unit

8 Which space probe took the first close-up photographs of the Moon's surface?

- (a) Hiten
- (b) Surveyor 3
- (c) Ranger 7
- (d) Luna 13

9 Uranus and Neptune are categorized as which type of planets?

- (a) Cold planets
- (b) Hot lava planets
- (c) Barren planets
- (d) Ice giants

10 The *Mars Reconnaissance Orbiter* has been orbiting Mars since…

- (a) 2006
- (b) 2002
- (c) 1999
- (d) 2007

Difficulty level: **Medium**

11 *Lunokhod 1* was the first remote-controlled rover to land on the Moon. What does the word "lunokhod" mean?

| Moon buggy | Moon rider | b |
| Moon racer | Moon walker | d |

12 Which of the giant planets appears brighter than the brightest star, Sirius?

| Uranus | Jupiter | b |
| Neptune | Saturn | d |

13 Which is the innermost ring of Saturn?

| C ring | D ring | b |
| B ring | A ring | d |

14 What is the name of the largest galaxy survey to be conducted before 2011?

| DEEP2 Redshift | Sloan Digital Sky | b |
| Two Micron All Sky | 2dF Galaxy Redshift | d |

15 Which type of comet is Halley's Comet?

| Long-range | Short-period | b |
| Long-term | Short-range | d |

16 Which unit is used to measure the mass of stars and galaxies?

| Solar mass | Solar unit | b |
| Solar tonne | Solar bulk | d |

17 Which spacecraft was the first to penetrate the atmosphere of Venus?

| a | Magellan | Pioneer Venus | b |
| c | Marineer 10 | Venera | d |

18 Astronomers use declination and which other co-ordinate for locating celestial objects?

| a | Latitude | Right ascension | b |
| c | Longitude | Left ascension | d |

19 In 2006 Saturn eclipsed the Sun. Which space probe took this image of this event?

| a | Hubble | Pioneer | b |
| c | Cassini | Voyager | d |

20 Titan is the largest of which planet's moons?

| a | Jupiter | Uranus | b |
| c | Mars | Saturn | d |

1 Which planet in the "Goldilocks zone", or habitable zone around a star, is classified as super-Earth?

a | Gliese 581a
b | Gliese 581c
c | Ceres
d | Makemake

2 A remnant emission from the Big Bang is described as what sort of background?

a | Cosmic microwave
b | Cosmic dust
c | Interstellar dust
d | Zodiacal light

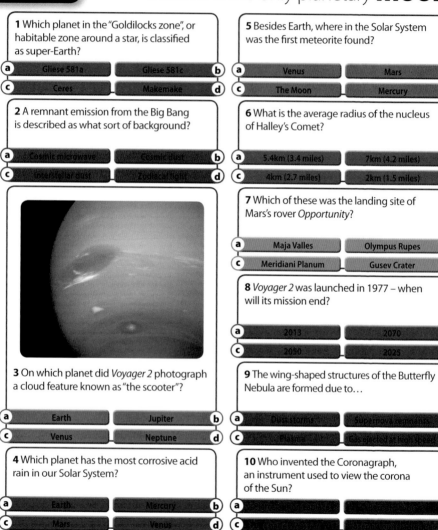

3 On which planet did *Voyager 2* photograph a cloud feature known as "the scooter"?

a | Earth
b | Jupiter
c | Venus
d | Neptune

4 Which planet has the most corrosive acid rain in our Solar System?

a | Earth
b | Mercury
c | Mars
d | Venus

5 Besides Earth, where in the Solar System was the first meteorite found?

a | Venus
b | Mars
c | The Moon
d | Mercury

6 What is the average radius of the nucleus of Halley's Comet?

a | 5.4km (3.4 miles)
b | 7km (4.2 miles)
c | 4km (2.7 miles)
d | 2km (1.5 miles)

7 Which of these was the landing site of Mars's rover *Opportunity*?

a | Maja Valles
b | Olympus Rupes
c | Meridiani Planum
d | Gusev Crater

8 *Voyager 2* was launched in 1977 – when will its mission end?

a | 2013
b | 2070
c | 2050
d | 2025

9 The wing-shaped structures of the Butterfly Nebula are formed due to…

a | Dust storms
b | Supernova remnants
c | Plasma
d | Gas ejected at high speed

10 Who invented the Coronagraph, an instrument used to view the corona of the Sun?

a |
b |
c |
d |

11 Tranquility, Serenity, and Nectar are names of maria (sea-like plains). Where are they located?

Titania	Ganymede	**b**
The Moon	Phobos	**d**

12 Which spacecraft carried *Lunokhod 1*, the first remote-controlled rover to land on the Moon?

Luna 1	Luna 17	**b**
Luna 8	Luna 15	**d**

13 The rate at which the Universe is expanding is given by the…

Hertz constant	Heisenberg constant	**b**
Hubble constant	Hahn constant	**d**

14 Which is the only giant planet whose equator is nearly at a right angle to its orbit?

Neptune	Uranus	**b**
Jupiter	Saturn	**d**

15 How many Solar System planets have rings?

2	5	**b**
4	3	**d**

16 More than 75 per cent of Venus's surface is covered by…

Craters	Oceans	**b**
Volcanic plains	Volcanoes	**d**

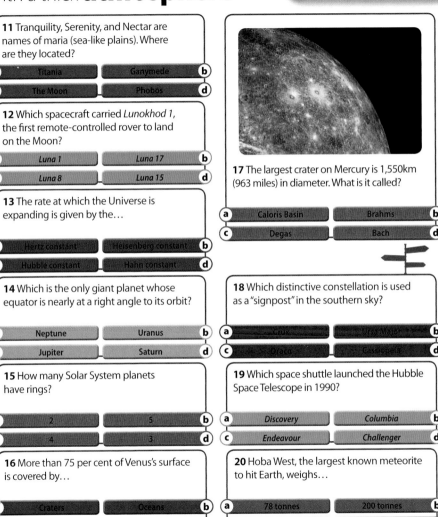

17 The largest crater on Mercury is 1,550km (963 miles) in diameter. What is it called?

a	Caloris Basin	Brahms	**b**
c	Degas	Bach	**d**

18 Which distinctive constellation is used as a "signpost" in the southern sky?

a	Crux	Ursa Major	**b**
c	Draco	Cassiopeia	**d**

19 Which space shuttle launched the Hubble Space Telescope in 1990?

a	*Discovery*	*Columbia*	**b**
c	*Endeavour*	*Challenger*	**d**

20 Hoba West, the largest known meteorite to hit Earth, weighs…

a	78 tonnes	200 tonnes	**b**
c	53 tonnes	66 tonnes	**d**

There are about **66 tota**

1 In which year did humans first land on the Moon?

- **a** 1969
- **b** 1956
- **c** 1976
- **d** 1989

2 Which is the most abundant chemical element in the Universe?

- **a** Oxygen
- **b** Hydrogen
- **c** Calcium
- **d** Helium

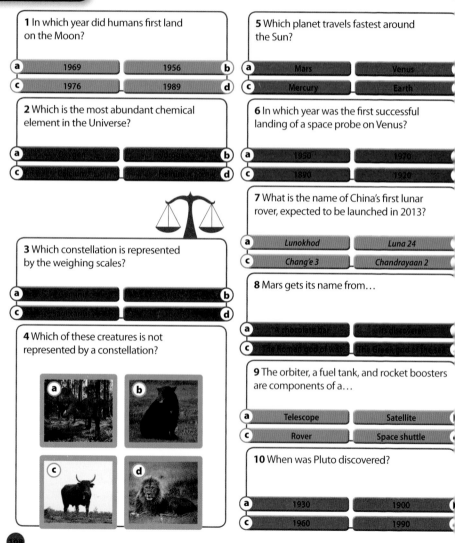

3 Which constellation is represented by the weighing scales?

- **a**
- **b**
- **c**
- **d**

4 Which of these creatures is not represented by a constellation?

- **a**
- **b**
- **c**
- **d**

5 Which planet travels fastest around the Sun?

- **a** Mars
- **b** Venus
- **c** Mercury
- **d** Earth

6 In which year was the first successful landing of a space probe on Venus?

- **a** 1950
- **b** 1970
- **c** 1890
- **d** 1920

7 What is the name of China's first lunar rover, expected to be launched in 2013?

- **a** Lunokhod
- **b** Luna 24
- **c** Chang'e 3
- **d** Chandrayaan 2

8 Mars gets its name from…

- **a** A chocolate bar
- **b** Its discoverer
- **c** The Roman god of war
- **d** The Greek god of the sea

9 The orbiter, a fuel tank, and rocket boosters are components of a…

- **a** Telescope
- **b** Satellite
- **c** Rover
- **d** Space shuttle

10 When was Pluto discovered?

- **a** 1930
- **b** 1900
- **c** 1960
- **d** 1990

11 Jupiter's largest moon is called Ganymede. Who was Ganymede?

- Greek god
- **b** Trojan prince
- Roman damsel
- **d** Mermaid

12 Which of these are also known as "dirty snowballs"?

- Comets
- **b** Dwarf planets
- Meteors
- **d** Asteroids

13 During which celestial phenomenon does the Sun appear as a bright ring around the Moon?

- **a** Annular phase
- **b** Annular eclipse
- **c** Total solar eclipse
- **d** Partial solar eclipse

14 Which planet is sometimes described as Earth's twin?

- **a** Mars
- **b** Mercury
- **c** Jupiter
- **d** Venus

15 This man is Yuri Gagarin. What is his claim to fame?

- **a** Built the first rocket
- **b** Landed on the Moon
- **c** First man to Mars
- **d** First man in space

NEAR–Shoemaker is the firs

1 When two stars orbit each other, what is it called?

- **a** Stellar rotation
- **b** Binary rotation
- **c** Orbiting system
- **d** Binary system

2 What is the scientific term for the twinkling of stars?

- **a** Stellar glow
- **b** Star splendour
- **c** Stellar sparkle
- **d** Stellar scintillation

3 This is the first television image from space. When was it taken?

- **a** 1 April 1960
- **b** 7 August 1962
- **c** 25 May 1967
- **d** 15 November 1970

4 How much would 6kg (13lb) of apples weigh on the Moon?

- **a** 1kg (2lb)
- **b** 3kg (7lb)
- **c** 6kg (13lb)
- **d** 12kg (26lb)

5 The world's governing body of astronomy is called the International…

- **a** Astronomy Federation
- **b** Astronomical Union
- **c** Astronomy Association
- **d** Astronomical Survey

6 Other than Pluto, how many dwarf planets are present in the Solar System?

- **a** 5
- **b** 2
- **c** 4
- **d** 3

7 What is the National Aeronautics and Space Administration commonly known as?

- **a** NASPA
- **b** NAESA
- **c** NASA
- **d** NRSC

8 Spider-like channels near Mars's south pole are formed due to the release of what from the ground?

- **a** Gas
- **b** Lava
- **c** Sulphuric acid
- **d** Water

9 Which comet slammed into Jupiter in 1994?

- **a** Hyakutake
- **b** Hale–Bopp
- **c** Shoemaker–Levy 9
- **d** Halley

10 Meteorites that are collected after being seen falling are called…

- **a** Meteorite falls
- **b** Finds
- **c** Discoveries
- **d** Meteorite debris

11 Which of Saturn's moons has a substantial atmosphere?

Dione	Rhea **b**
Hyperion	Titan **d**

12 What does NEO stand for?

Next-to-Earth Orientation	Non-Earth Orbit **b**
New Earth Order	Near-Earth Objects **d**

13 When did *Mars Odyssey* start looking for water on Mars?

1995	2005 **b**
1999	2002 **d**

14 Which is the largest and brightest star-forming region visible in the night sky?

Orion Nebula	Eagle Nebula **b**
Omega Nebula	Pelican Nebula **d**

15 Which planet is the richest in iron?

Venus	Mercury **b**
Earth	Mars **d**

16 Arachnoids – a series of concentric circular or oval fractures – are a feature on which planet?

Jupiter	Earth **b**
Venus	Mars **d**

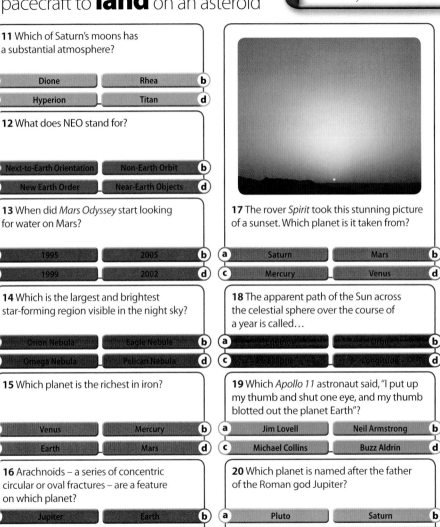

17 The rover *Spirit* took this stunning picture of a sunset. Which planet is it taken from?

a Saturn	Mars **b**
c Mercury	Venus **d**

18 The apparent path of the Sun across the celestial sphere over the course of a year is called…

a Equinox	Orbit **b**
c Ecliptic	Longitude **d**

19 Which *Apollo 11* astronaut said, "I put up my thumb and shut one eye, and my thumb blotted out the planet Earth"?

a Jim Lovell	Neil Armstrong **b**
c Michael Collins	Buzz Aldrin **d**

20 Which planet is named after the father of the Roman god Jupiter?

a Pluto	Saturn **b**
c Mercury	Mars **d**

1 Which impact crater on Mercury is believed to have been created in a giant asteroid strike approximately four billion years ago?

a Bach
b Caloris Basin
c Brahms
d Degas

2 Which distinctive constellation is used as a "signpost" in the northern sky?

a
b
c
d

3 How many Lagrangian points are there in the Earth–Moon–Sun system?

a 8
b 5
c 6
d 7

4 On average, what depth of surface material is lost from Halley's Comet on each orbit?

a 1m (3ft)
b 3m (10ft)
c 5m (16ft)
d 2m (7ft)

5 The Sun's corona can be viewed through which instrument?

a
b
c
d

6 Who was the youngest person to travel to space, at 25 years of age?

a Yang Liwei
b Gherman Titov
c John Glenn
d Valeri Polyakov

7 The *New Horizons* spacecraft is set to send pictures back from where in 2015?

a The Sun
b Saturn
c Pluto
d Mercury

8 What accumulates in black holes, causing quasars to shine so brightly?

a
b
c
d

9 Which of Uranus's moons has one of the most varied landscapes, with deep canyons and smooth plains?

a Miranda
b Titania
c Oberon
d Umbriel

10 What is the axial tilt of Mercury, pictured here?

a 90°
b 40°
c
d

11 The *Opportunity* rover found small, spherical grains containing hematite. What were they nicknamed?

Blueberries	Cherries **b**
Gooseberries	Red currants **d**

12 Which was NASA's first human spaceflight programme?

Mercury	Apollo **b**
Gemini	Apollo-Soyuz **d**

13 A superdense point in space where the normal laws of physics do not apply is called…

Lagrangian point	Event horizon **b**
Accretion disc	Singularity **d**

14 This barred spiral galaxy, NGC 6872, is located in the constellation Pavo. Which is Pavo's brightest star?

	b
	d

15 What is the Japanese Experiment Module (JEM), the largest module of the ISS, popularly known as?

a Kaguya	Akatsuki **b**
c Okina	Kibō **d**

16 Which 200km- (124-mile-) wide impact crater was created near Mexico 65 million years ago?

a Beaverhead	Shoemaker **b**
c Chicxulub	Vredefort **d**

17 In 1995 which SETI programme began observations in Australia to search for signals from other civilizations in space?

a SERENDIP	Project Phoenix **b**
c Project BAMBI	setiQuest **d**

18 Charles Messier published a catalogue of which astronomical objects based on his observations?

a	**b**
c	**d**

19 Which Dutch scientist discovered Saturn's largest moon, Titan, in 1655?

a Walter Lewin	Johann Stein **b**
c Petrus Plancius	Christiaan Huygens **d**

20 Which of these galaxies is the nearest to the Milky Way?

a Boötes Dwarf	Sculptor Dwarf **b**
c Sagittarius Dwarf	Large Magellanic Cloud **d**

There are **88 constellations**

1 What is the outermost region of the atmosphere surrounding a star called?

a)
b)
c)
d)

2 The Sun contains what percentage of the total mass of the Solar System?

a) 15 per cent
b) 65 per cent
c) 99.8 per cent
d) 50 per cent

3 What is Wild 2?

a) Comet
b) Asteroid
c) Meteorite
d) Dwarf planet

4 The lead singer of the rock band Queen shared a name with which rocky planet?

a) Mercury
b) Earth
c) Venus
d) Mars

5 What did the Romans call the Moon?

a) Luna
b) Mani
c) Selene
d) Ganymede

6 Which event caused the Universe to come into being about 13.7 billion years ago?

a) The Solar System formed
b) The Sun formed
c) The Big Bang
d) The Big Crunch

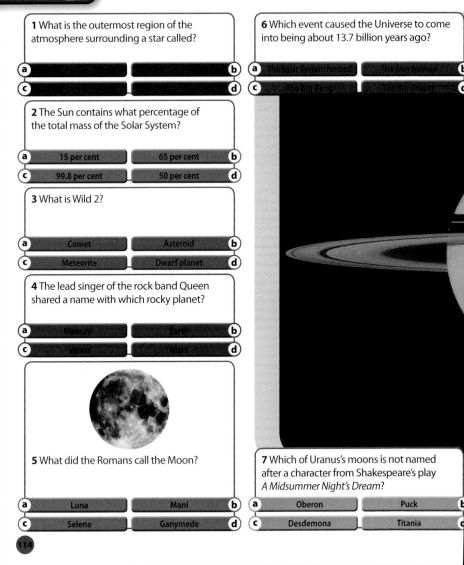

7 Which of Uranus's moons is not named after a character from Shakespeare's play *A Midsummer Night's Dream*?

a) Oberon
b) Puck
c) Desdemona
d) Titania

8 Which planet is shown here?

Jupiter	Mercury **b**
Uranus	Saturn **d**

9 The nucleus, the coma, and the tail are parts of a…

a Meteorite	Comet **b**
c Asteroid	Meteor **d**

10 Which two dogs were the first survivors of a trip to space and back?

a Anita and Arabella	Belka and Strelka **b**
c Laika and Ham	Dolly and Bruno **d**

11 What does ISS stand for?

a Interplanetary Space Stop	International Star Station **b**
c International Space Station	Intermediate Stellar Station **d**

12 Penumbra and umbra are light and dark regions of…

a Sunspots	The Moon **b**
c Milky Way	Proxima Centauri **d**

13 Which planet's rotation period is the longest in the Solar System?

a Jupiter	Mars **b**
c Uranus	Venus **d**

14 What colour are sunspots?

a White	Black **b**
c Orange	Red **d**

15 Which character from the blockbuster animated film *Toy Story* was inspired by an *Apollo 11* astronaut?

a Mr Potato Head	Woody **b**
c Rex	Buzz Lightyear **d**

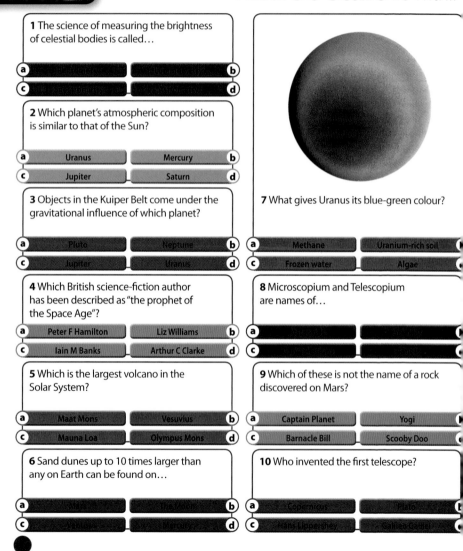

1 The science of measuring the brightness of celestial bodies is called…

(a) ▮▮▮▮▮▮▮▮▮ (b) ▮▮▮▮▮▮▮▮▮

(c) ▮▮▮▮▮▮▮▮▮ (d) ▮▮▮▮▮▮▮▮▮

2 Which planet's atmospheric composition is similar to that of the Sun?

(a) Uranus (b) Mercury

(c) Jupiter (d) Saturn

3 Objects in the Kuiper Belt come under the gravitational influence of which planet?

(a) Pluto (b) Neptune

(c) Jupiter (d) Uranus

4 Which British science-fiction author has been described as "the prophet of the Space Age"?

(a) Peter F Hamilton (b) Liz Williams

(c) Iain M Banks (d) Arthur C Clarke

5 Which is the largest volcano in the Solar System?

(a) Maat Mons (b) Vesuvius

(c) Mauna Loa (d) Olympus Mons

6 Sand dunes up to 10 times larger than any on Earth can be found on…

(a) Mars (b) The Moon

(c) Venus (d) Mercury

7 What gives Uranus its blue-green colour?

(a) Methane | Uranium-rich soil

(c) Frozen water | Algae

8 Microscopium and Telescopium are names of…

(a) ▮▮▮▮▮▮▮▮▮ | ▮▮▮▮▮▮▮▮▮

(c) ▮▮▮▮▮▮▮▮▮ | ▮▮▮▮▮▮▮▮▮

9 Which of these is not the name of a rock discovered on Mars?

(a) Captain Planet | Yogi

(c) Barnacle Bill | Scooby Doo

10 Who invented the first telescope?

(a) Copernicus | Plato

(c) Hans Lippershey | Galileo Galilei

11 Approximately how hot is the surface of the Sun?

100,000°C (180,032°F) | 250,000°C (450,032°F) **(b)**
6,000°C (10,832°F) | 95,000°C (171,032°F) **(d)**

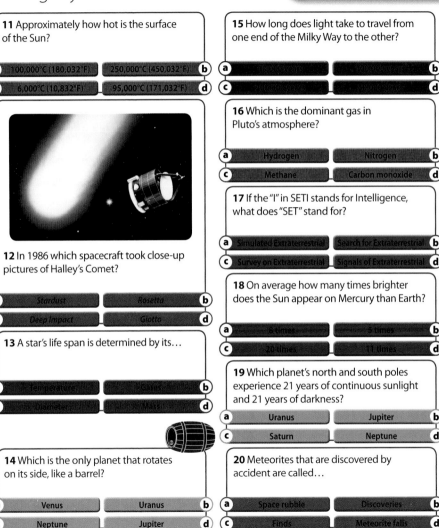

12 In 1986 which spacecraft took close-up pictures of Halley's Comet?

Stardust | Rosetta **(b)**
Deep Impact | Giotto **(d)**

13 A star's life span is determined by its…

Temperature | Gases **(b)**
Diameter | Mass **(d)**

14 Which is the only planet that rotates on its side, like a barrel?

Venus | Uranus **(b)**
Neptune | Jupiter **(d)**

15 How long does light take to travel from one end of the Milky Way to the other?

(a) 10,000 years | 100,000 years **(b)**
(c) 200,000 years | 50,000 years **(d)**

16 Which is the dominant gas in Pluto's atmosphere?

(a) Hydrogen | Nitrogen **(b)**
(c) Methane | Carbon monoxide **(d)**

17 If the "I" in SETI stands for Intelligence, what does "SET" stand for?

(a) Simulated Extraterrestrial | Search for Extraterrestrial **(b)**
(c) Survey on Extraterrestrial | Signals of Extraterrestrial **(d)**

18 On average how many times brighter does the Sun appear on Mercury than Earth?

(a) 8 times | 5 times **(b)**
(c) 20 times | 11 times **(d)**

19 Which planet's north and south poles experience 21 years of continuous sunlight and 21 years of darkness?

(a) Uranus | Jupiter **(b)**
(c) Saturn | Neptune **(d)**

20 Meteorites that are discovered by accident are called…

(a) Space rubble | Discoveries **(b)**
(c) Finds | Meteorite falls **(d)**

1 Which rover(s) confirmed that Mars had widespread and long-lived oceans in the past?

a Spirit and Opportunity

b Sojourner

c Discovery

d Spirit and Pathfinder

2 Which was the first spacecraft to orbit the Sun successfully?

a Pioneer 9

b Venera 7

c Columbia

d Luna 1

3 At what rate is the Moon drifting away from Earth?

a 4m (13ft) a year

b 4km (2 miles) a year

c 4cm (2in) a year

d 4mm (0.1in) a year

4 Which was the first exoplanet to be imaged in visible light?

a Pegasi b

b Gliese d

c Beta Pectoris b

d Formalhaut b

5 Which of these moons does not belong to Uranus?

a Rosalind

b Ophelia

c Larissa

d Portia

6 Which famous science-fiction author penned the classic collection of short stories, *I, Robot*?

a H G Wells

b Ray Bradbury

c Jules Verne

d Isaac Asimov

7 Which is the largest galaxy in the Local Group?

a Andromeda Galaxy

b Milky Way

c Aquarius Dwarf

d SagDIG

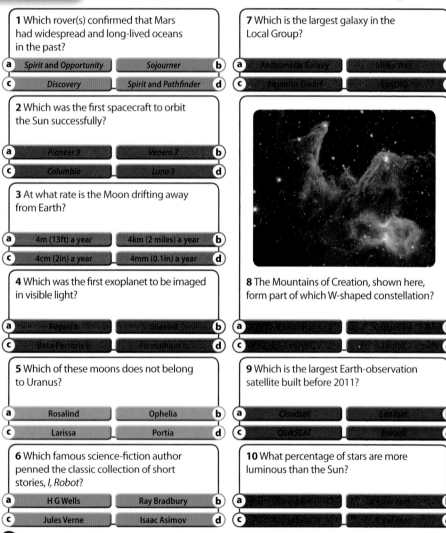

8 The Mountains of Creation, shown here, form part of which W-shaped constellation?

a Cassiopeia

c Cetus

d Taurus

9 Which is the largest Earth-observation satellite built before 2011?

a Cloudsat

b Landsat

c QuikSCAT

d Envisat

10 What percentage of stars are more luminous than the Sun?

11 Which is the world's largest telescope, measuring 305m (1,000ft) across?

a) Magellan
b) Keck telescope
c) Arecibo radio telescope
d) James Lick telescope

12 Which spacecraft flew close to asteroid Lutetia in July 2010?

a) Rosetta
b) Martha
c) Betty
d) Renée

13 Who is the oldest person to have travelled on a spacecraft, at the age of 77?

a) Yuri Gagarin
b) Mae Jemison
c) John Glenn
d) Gherman Titov

14 In which year were the first of Uranus's rings identified?

a) 1985
b) 1977
c) 2000
d) 1980

15 Russian cosmonaut Valeri Polyakov spent a record number of days in space. How long was he there for?

a) 452.1 days
b) 437.7 days
c) 365.9 days
d) 100 days

16 The rays that are emitted when the gas in the Sun's corona heats up to several million degrees are called…

a) Ultraviolet rays
b) X-rays
c) Infrared rays
d) Gamma rays

17 Which is the brightest star in the constellation Scorpius?

a)
b)
c)
d)

18 Which galaxy of the Local Group is the furthest from the Milky Way?

a) Antlia Dwarf
b) Pegasus Dwarf
c) Sextans B
d) Sextans A

19 Who was the first and the only geologist to land on the Moon?

a) Harrison Schmitt
b) Buzz Aldrin
c) Pete Conrad
d) David Scott

20 Which was the first privately financed spacecraft to officially make it into space?

a) Spacelab One
b) SpaceShipOne
c) Air Force One
d) Space Flight One

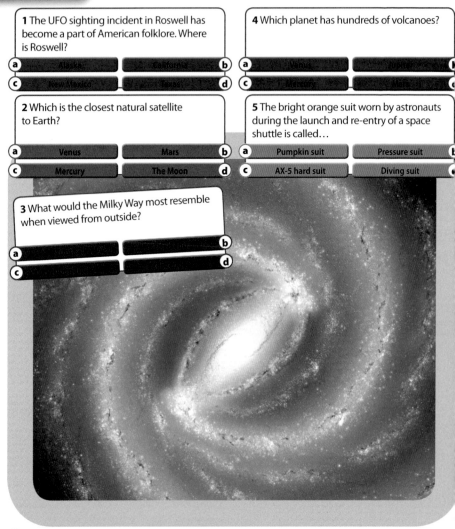

1 The UFO sighting incident in Roswell has become a part of American folklore. Where is Roswell?

(a) Alaska   (b) California
(c) New Mexico   (d) Texas

2 Which is the closest natural satellite to Earth?

(a) Venus   (b) Mars
(c) Mercury   (d) The Moon

3 What would the Milky Way most resemble when viewed from outside?

(a)   (b)
(c)   (d)

4 Which planet has hundreds of volcanoes?

(a) Venus   (b) Jupiter
(c) Mercury   (d) Mars

5 The bright orange suit worn by astronauts during the launch and re-entry of a space shuttle is called…

(a) Pumpkin suit   (b) Pressure suit
(c) AX-5 hard suit   (d) Diving suit

6 Which planet has the largest set of rings?

| Uranus | Neptune **b** |
| Saturn | Jupiter **d** |

7 How many planets are there in the Solar System?

| 6 | 9 **b** |
| 8 | 7 **d** |

8 Which is the hottest planet?

| Mars | Jupiter **b** |
| Venus | Earth **d** |

9 Which country launched the first ever artificial satellite?

| Germany | Russia **b** |
| US | UK **d** |

10 Which *Harry Potter* character shares a name with the Dog Star?

| Sirius Black **a** | Dedalus Diggle **b** |
| Draco Malfoy **c** | Seamus Finnigan **d** |

11 How many dwarf planets have been recognized so far?

| 2 **a** | 5 **b** |
| 7 **c** | 9 **d** |

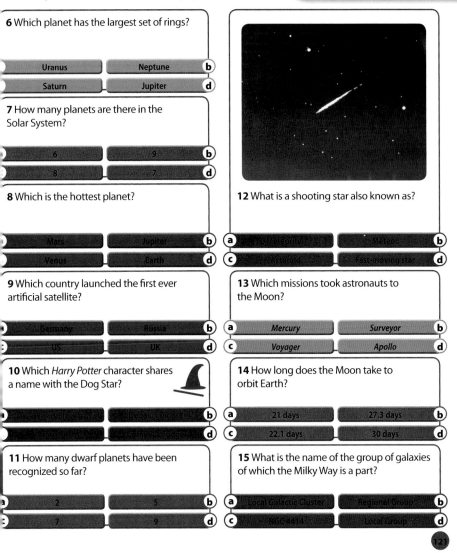

12 What is a shooting star also known as?

| **a** Meteorite | Meteor **b** |
| **c** Asteroid | Fast-moving star **d** |

13 Which missions took astronauts to the Moon?

| **a** Mercury | Surveyor **b** |
| **c** Voyager | Apollo **d** |

14 How long does the Moon take to orbit Earth?

| **a** 21 days | 27.3 days **b** |
| **c** 22.1 days | 30 days **d** |

15 What is the name of the group of galaxies of which the Milky Way is a part?

| **a** Local Galactic Cluster | Regional Group **b** |
| **c** NGC 4414 | Local Group **d** |

1 How long did it take *Sputnik 1* to orbit Earth once?

- **a** 98 hours
- **b** 98 weeks
- **c** 98 minutes
- **d** 98 days

2 The combined mass of all asteroids in the Asteroid Belt equals…

- **a** 4 per cent of the Moon
- **b** 10 per cent of Earth
- **c** 23 per cent of Jupiter
- **d** 8 per cent of Venus

3 When *Mariner 9* arrived at Mars in 1971, it had to delay taking photographs because the surface was hidden by…

- **a** Fog
- **b** A heat haze
- **c** Clouds
- **d** A dust storm

4 In which year did astronomers discover radio waves emanating from space?

- **a**
- **b**
- **c**
- **d**

5 In which area of a spiral galaxy are new stars constantly formed?

- **a** Spiral arms
- **b** Outer rims
- **c** Outer core
- **d** Central hub

6 When was Pluto re-classified as a dwarf planet?

- **a** 2010
- **b** 2006
- **c** 2004
- **d** 2000

7 Who is the author of the popular science-fiction novel *2001: A Space Odyssey*?

- **a** Arthur C Clarke
- **b** Isaac Asimov
- **c** Robert A Heinlein
- **d** Ray Cummings

8 At what speed, per second, does Earth orbit the Sun?

- **a** 30km (19 miles)
- **b** 300m (948ft)
- **c** 2km (1 mile)
- **d** 10km (6 miles)

9 Who named Uranus, the seventh planet in the Solar System?

- **a** John Herschel
- **b** King George III
- **c** Johann Bode
- **d** William Herschel

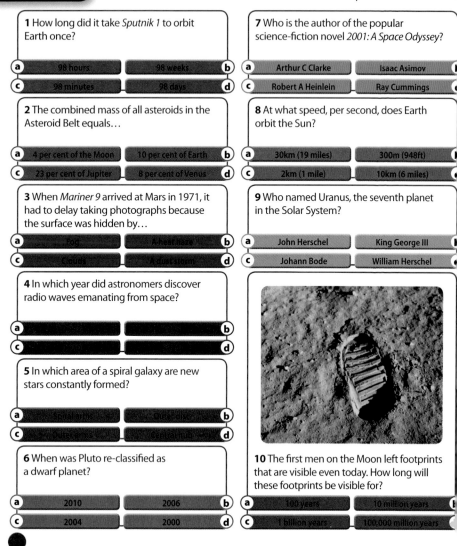

10 The first men on the Moon left footprints that are visible even today. How long will these footprints be visible for?

- **a** 100 years
- **b** 10 million years
- **c** 1 billion years
- **d** 100,000 million years

…each **Pluto** in **2015**

Difficulty level: **Medium**

11 What did Galileo Galilei compare Saturn's rings to when he discovered them in 1610?

| Eyes | Balls (b) |
| Ear lobes | Loaf of bread (d) |

12 When did the *Galileo* space mission to Jupiter end?

| 1975 | 2003 (b) |
| 1990 | 2010 (d) |

13 What is the bright red star in the constellation Orion called?

14 What was *Apollo's* Lunar Roving Vehicle popularly called?

| Moon sled | Moon transporter (b) |
| Moon buggy | Lunar scooter (d) |

15 Which of the following asteroids has been promoted to dwarf planet status?

| Vesta | Gaspra (b) |
| Annefrank | Ceres (d) |

16 Which planet is the most distant of the five planets easily visible to the naked eye?

| Neptune | Saturn (b) |
| Uranus | Mercury (d) |

17 Which spacecraft, shown here, first photographed the Moon's far side?

| (a) Apollo 17 | Luna 3 (b) |
| (c) Apollo 8 | Apollo 16 (d) |

18 Uranus's moons are named after characters in…

| (a) Science-fiction films | Cartoons (b) |
| (c) Famous musicals | English literature (d) |

19 What is the approximate age of the Sun?

| (a) 6.3 billion years | 3.7 billion years (b) |
| (c) 5.9 billion years | 4.6 billion years (d) |

20 Which of these rockets was used to send man to the Moon?

| (a) Titan | Saturn V (b) |
| (c) Atlas | Redstone (d) |

123

1 What is interstellar medium made up of?

(a) ░░░░░░░░░░░░ (b) ░░░░░░░░░░░░
(c) ░░░░░░░░░░░░ (d) ░░░░░░░░░░░░

2 Which astronomer identified up to 70 of the first 100 exoplanets discovered?

(a) Clyde Tombaugh (b) Bill Oddie
(c) Geoffrey Marcy (d) George Gamow

3 American musician Moby had a hit with the space-inspired song "We're all made of…"

(a) Water (b) Stars
(c) Dark matter (d) Comets

4 The measure of brightness of a celestial body, as seen from Earth, is called…

(a) Apparent magnitude (b) Absolute magnitude
(c) Bolometric magnitude (d) ░░░░░░░░░░░░

5 How many states are members of the European Space Agency (ESA)?

(a) 10 (b) 50
(c) 19 (d) 25

6 What is the Cassini Division?

(a) Star classification system (b) Area around a black hole
(c) Gap in Saturn's rings (d) Gap between planets

7 Which British scientist discovered the first pulsar?

(a) ░░░░░░░░░░░░ (b) ░░░░░░░░░░░░
(c) ░░░░░░░░░░░░

8 The first global map of Venus's surface was produced by…

(a) Mariner 2 (b) Multiprobe
(c) Venus Express (d) Pioneer Venus Orbiter

9 Which is the largest and most powerful rocket ever built?

(a) Juno 1 (b) Saturn V
(c) Ariane 5 (d) Long March 2C

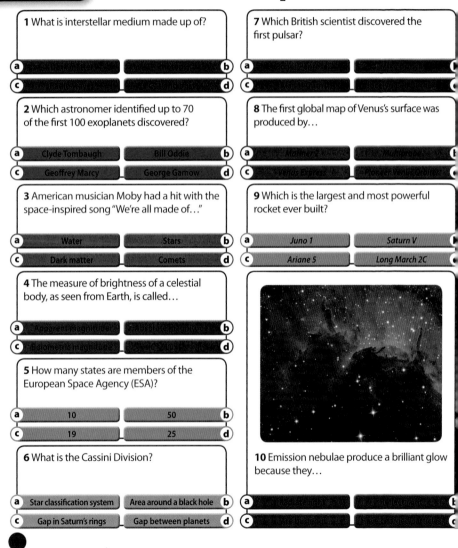

10 Emission nebulae produce a brilliant glow because they…

(a) ░░░░░░░░░░░░ (b) ░░░░░░░░░░░░
(c) ░░░░░░░░░░░░ (c) ░░░░░░░░░░░░

11 Which of the following was a prototype of a Single-Stage-to-Orbit launch vehicle?

Saturn V	Mir **b**
SpaceShipOne	VentureStar **d**

12 NGC is a comprehensive catalogue of nebulae, clusters, and galaxies. What does NGC stand for?

	b
	d

13 Which of these is one of the most luminous stars known?

	b
Pistol Star	The Sun **d**

14 Which satellites are capable of seeing detail less than 1m (3ft) across on Earth?

Navigation satellites	Spy satellites **b**
Remote-sensing satellites	Meteorological satellites **d**

15 In 2000 American rock band No Doubt released an album called *Return of*…

Uranus	Jupiter **b**
Neptune	Saturn **d**

16 Which rocket series launched all 12 of NASA's *Gemini* missions?

Titan II	Saturn V **b**
Atlas	Saturn IB **d**

17 Which is the most volcanically active body in the Solar System?

a Neptune	Io **b**
c Uranus	Titan **d**

18 The first active volcanic site discovered on Jupiter's moon Io is named after which Hawaiian volcano goddess?

a Pele	Uliuli **b**
c Tapo	Hina **d**

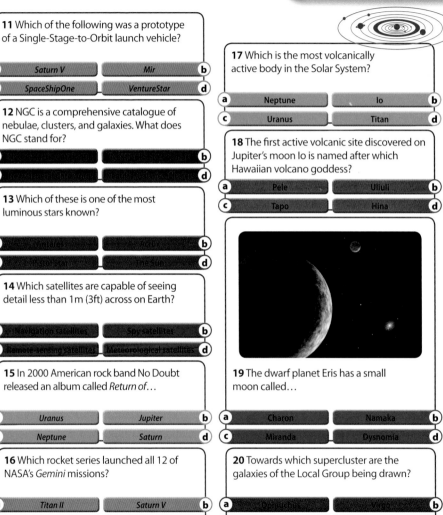

19 The dwarf planet Eris has a small moon called…

a Charon	Namaka **b**
c Miranda	Dysnomia **d**

20 Towards which supercluster are the galaxies of the Local Group being drawn?

a Ophiuchus	Virgo **b**
c Shapley	Perseus-Pisces **d**

Universe of galaxies

The Universe is made up of everything that we know about and everything yet to be discovered. As we look into it from our home planet, Earth, we see more planets, as well as other space objects such as the Sun and the distant stars. These all exist in the Milky Way Galaxy. Beyond are thousands more galaxies – there are at least 125 billion scattered through the Universe.

Explosive start

Our Universe has not always existed. Scientists believe it came into existence about 13.7 billion years ago in a kind of explosion known as the Big Bang. Initially, the Universe was incredibly hot and consisted of energy. This very quickly turned to matter, which eventually formed stars and galaxies.

Thousands of galaxies occupy this tiny area of Earth's sky

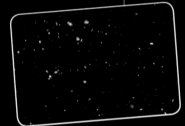

Galaxies galore

Galaxies are huge collections of millions or billions of stars, along with vast amounts of gas and dust. They occur wherever we look in space. Viewing the Universe from the outside, we would see that they make huge, web-like networks stretching through space.

Background heat

Looking into space, we look back in time. This is because light from distant galaxies takes millions of years to reach us. We cannot look as far back as the Big Bang, but we have detected and mapped its decaying heat (right) from when the Universe was about 380,000 years old.

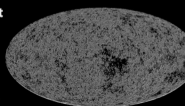

Colliding galaxies

The Universe has been cooling, expanding, and changing ever since its start. Galaxies have evolved through collisions and interactions, changing characteristics such as size and shape. Two galaxies known as the Antennae (above), after the faint streamers of stars stretching from them, began to collide about 700 million years ago.

Andromeda Galaxy

Galaxies come in four main shapes and a range of sizes. Spiral and barred-spiral galaxies are disc-shaped, with arms of stars winding out from a round or bar-shaped centre. Elliptical galaxies are ball-shaped, from nearly spherical to flattened oval. Irregular galaxies have no regular shape. The nearest large galaxy is the spiral-shaped Andromeda.

The Milky Way

From our position inside the Milky Way, it is difficult to make out our galaxy's structure. Astronomers believe it is a barred spiral, and that we are in one of its spiral arms. Many of the galaxy's stars appear as a milky path of light across our night sky – this is also called the Milky Way.

Stars

The stars in Earth's night sky are so distant that they appear as pinpoints of light. Astronomers tell them apart using a system of 88 constellations. Up close, the stars are huge, glowing, spinning balls of gas made mainly of hydrogen with helium. They differ in size, temperature, colour, luminosity, and mass, which change as the star ages.

Brilliant star

Sirius is the brightest star in Earth's night sky. Its brightness depends on how much light the star produces – its luminosity – and also its distance from Earth. Placed next to the Sun, Sirius would be 25 times brighter.

Patterns in the sky

Each constellation includes a pattern made by linking stars with imaginary lines. The patterns are in the shape of humans, creatures, or objects. Some, such as Orion the hunter, who holds a club and a lion's pelt, feature in Greek mythology.

Star birth

Stars do not live forever but, like humans, have a life cycle. They come into existence inside huge clouds of mostly hydrogen with helium. Parts of the cloud collapse, spin, and form spheres – young stars. Nuclear reactions start in their hot, dense centres and produce energy.

Clustered together

Stars form in clusters, which slowly drift apart.
The Pleiades cluster (right) will disperse in
the next 250 million years. Yet some stars
always stay together, co-existing with one
or two companions. Only about half
of all nearby stars are alone.

Star death

A star's lifespan and death depend on the star's
mass – the amount of material it is made of.
Stars like the Sun mature into red giants, then
planetary nebulae, and end up as white dwarfs.
More massive stars explode and become a
neutron star or black hole.

Cloud fragments
form stars

Nuclear reactions in
stars produce light

Mature star
sheds material

Stellar recycling

Material discarded by dying stars
mixes with hydrogen between
the stars. Over millions of years
this mixed material forms clouds,
which in turn produce new stars.
As these stars mature and die they
scatter material that can be used to
produce a further generation of stars.

Cloud forms from
interstellar and star material

129

The Sun and the Solar System

The Sun and the large number of much smaller objects that orbit around it are together known as the Solar System. They have been together for about 4.6 billion years, ever since they formed from a huge, spinning cloud of gas and dust called the solar nebula. The Sun is made of 99.8 per cent of the system's material and its powerful gravity keeps the system together.

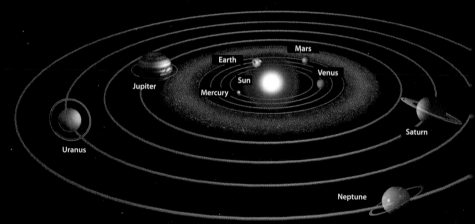

Mars

Earth

Venus

Jupiter

Sun

Mercury

Saturn

Uranus

Neptune

Centre of solar nebula becomes dense and heats up

A spinning disc of unused material surrounds the young Sun

Disc material joins to form planets

The Sun and its family

After the Sun, the largest Solar System objects are the eight planets, which between them have 168 moons. Smaller than the planets are five dwarf planets, billions of asteroids, Kuiper Belt objects, and comets.

Formation of the Solar System

The Solar System started to take shape when gravity pulled the solar nebula's material inwards. The nebula's centre became denser, heated up, and formed the Sun. Unused material bumped and joined and slowly formed the planets.

What's in a name?

Solar System objects are named according to guidelines. The planets are named after ancient gods and goddesses. Jupiter takes its name from the king of the Roman gods (left). Comets are named after their discoverers, and asteroids have a wide range of names, including those of astronomers, musicians, and fictional characters such as Pinocchio.

Local star

Earth is 149.6 million km (93 million miles) from the Sun, which is close enough for our local star to appear as a disc in our sky. Its surface temperature of 5,500°C (9,900°F) gives the Sun its yellow colour. It provides us with heat and light, and we use it to regulate our day and year.

Solar surface

Close to, the Sun is a violent, active place. Its visible surface, called its photosphere, consists of 1,000km-(620-mile-) wide cells of hot rising gas. Dark spots appear on its surface when the upward flow of hot gas is interrupted. These sunspots typically last for two months and are often bigger than Earth.

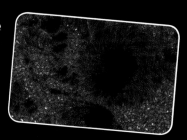

Sun's energy

Energy produced by nuclear reactions in the Sun's core is released through its surface. Short-lived jets of gas leap up constantly. Bursts of energy called flares also explode out of the surface. Giant clouds of gas that loop and arch into space are prominences that can last for months.

Rocky planets

Mercury, Venus, Earth, and Mars are the four smallest Solar System planets and the four closest to the Sun. Together they are known as the rocky planets. They are made of rock and metal, loosely divided into layers – metal in the centre and rocks in the mantle and crust above.

Different worlds

Although the four planets formed at the same time from the same material, they have developed into contrasting worlds. They were all bombarded by space rocks left over from the planet-making process, but the surfaces of Venus, Earth, and Mars have changed markedly over time.

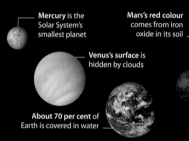

Mercury is the Solar System's smallest planet

Mars's red colour comes from iron oxide in its soil

Venus's surface is hidden by clouds

About 70 per cent of Earth is covered in water

Home planet

Earth is the largest rocky planet. Two things make it stand out from all other planets. Earth is the only place known to have liquid water, and it is home to at least 1.5 million distinct forms of life.

Cratered Mercury

Mercury is a grey, lifeless world. Its surface is covered by impact craters formed when space rocks bombarded the planet more than 3.5 billion years ago. It has the shortest planetary orbit round the Sun, completing one circuit every 88 days.

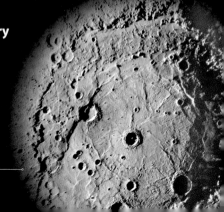

Rembrandt Crater is 720km (447 miles) across and pitted by smaller craters

Volcanic Venus

The unbroken blanket of cloud that surrounds Venus
traps the Sun's heat and makes it a scorching, suffocating world.
Spacecraft have revealed a surface largely covered in volcanic lava
that erupted and seeped from hundreds of volcanoes in the past.

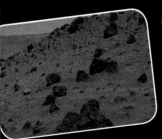

Mars, the red planet

More distant from the Sun than Earth, Mars has vast,
ice-cold, rocky deserts, and ice caps at its poles. The
Valles Marineris, a huge system of canyons, cuts across
its surface, and Mars is home to Olympus Mons,
the Solar System's largest volcano.

Earth's moon

The Moon is about one quarter Earth's size and
the closest space object to us. This dry, dead
ball of rock orbits round us and travels with our
planet as it makes its yearly orbit round the
Sun. The dark areas visible on its surface are
regions of solidified lava known as maria.

Giant planets

The planets Jupiter, Saturn, Uranus, and Neptune are giant-sized worlds. They lie beyond the Asteroid Belt between 5 and 30 times Earth's distance from the Sun. Looking at them, we see the tops of their deep, hydrogen-rich gas atmospheres. Underneath, they have liquid or semi-solid layers, and at their hearts, a rocky core. All four have rings and a large family of moons.

King of the planets

Jupiter is the largest and most massive planet. About 11 times Earth's size, it is made of 2.5 times the combined material of the other seven planets. It takes just under 10 hours to make one spin on its axis – the fastest of all the planets.

Huge storms appear as round and oval structures in Jupiter's atmosphere

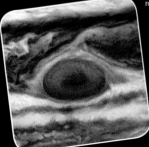

Great Red Spot

Jupiter's quick spin, combined with winds that blow round the planet, have helped form colourful bands in its upper atmosphere. White and dark spots amongst the bands are huge storms. The largest of them is the Great Red Spot, which has been observed on and off for more than 340 years.

Saturn, the ringed world

Pale yellow Saturn is encircled by a spectacular set of rings. First observed just over 400 years ago, these rings appear solid from a distance, but are made from millions of pieces of dirty water-ice, each one making its own orbit round the planet.

Uranus and Neptune

The nearest six planets to the Sun, Mercury to Saturn, have been known of since humans first studied the sky. The more distant planets, Uranus and Neptune, were both discovered within the last 240 years, using a telescope. Very similar in size, these cold worlds appear blue because of methane in their atmospheres.

Families of moons

The giants share more than 160 moons. These range in size from huge spherical bodies to irregular-shaped moons only a few kilometres across. Just bigger than Mercury, Titan (right) is Saturn's largest moon. A cold ice-and-rock world, it is surrounded by a honey-coloured atmosphere.

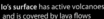

Io's surface has active volcanoes and is covered by lava flows

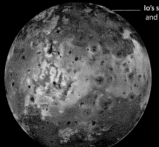

The Galileans

Jupiter has 63 moons, the most of any planet. The first to be discovered were its four largest. Known as the Galilean moons after Galileo Galilei, who observed them, these are Ganymede, Callisto, Io, and Europa. Ganymede is bigger than the planet Mercury and is the largest moon in the Solar System.

Belts and icy bodies

The many small objects that exist in the Solar System are unused material from when the planets formed. They are found in three main locations. Closest to the Sun are the asteroids that make up the Asteroid Belt between Mars and Jupiter. Dwarf planets and ice-and-rock objects form the Kuiper Belt beyond Neptune, and the more distant Oort Cloud consists of comets.

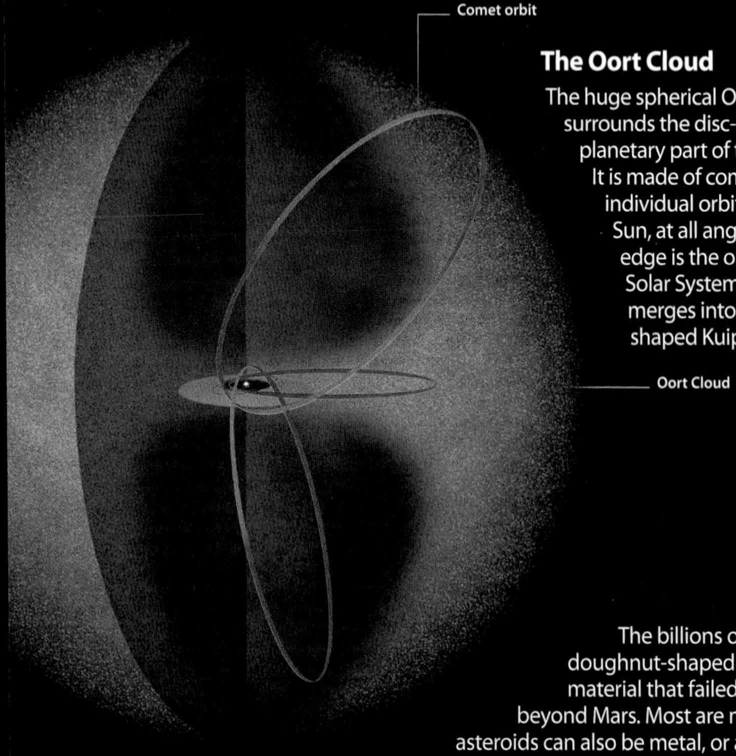

Comet orbit

The Oort Cloud

The huge spherical Oort Cloud surrounds the disc-shaped planetary part of the Solar System. It is made of comets following individual orbits around the Sun, at all angles. Its outer edge is the outer edge of the Solar System. Its inner edge merges into the doughnut-shaped Kuiper Belt.

Oort Cloud

Asteroids

The billions of asteroids in the doughnut-shaped Asteroid Belt are material that failed to form a planet beyond Mars. Most are made of rock, but asteroids can also be metal, or a mix of rock and metal. Almost all are irregular in shape, such as Ida (above), which is 58km (36 miles) long.

Pluto and the dwarf planets

The largest objects in the Kuiper Belt are the dwarf planets. The biggest is Eris; next comes Pluto (shown left), which has four moons orbiting it. Astronomers introduced the term "dwarf planet" in 2006 for almost-round objects that orbit the Sun within a belt of objects.

Comets

About a trillion comets exist in the Oort Cloud. Each is a city-wide nucleus, also known as a dirty snowball, because it is a mix of snow and rock dust. Occasionally one travels through the inner Solar System, undergoing a dramatic change as it develops a vast head and two tails.

Meteors

A fragment of comet dust or an asteroid that travels through Earth's atmosphere can produce a streak of light in Earth's night sky. This streak lasts for less than a second and is called a meteor or, more commonly, a shooting star.

Meteorites on Earth

A piece of asteroid that travels through our atmosphere and lands on Earth is known as a meteorite. Most fall in the ocean and are never found. But scientists regularly find them in Antarctica, where dark rock stands out against the white landscape.

Space travel

Rockets have been blasting off from Earth and sending craft into space for more than 60 years. They have launched hundreds of unmanned craft, as well as more than 500 astronauts, 24 of which travelled as far as the Moon. The unmanned, robotic craft have journeyed to all eight Solar System planets, as well as moons, asteroids and comets, and have approached the Sun.

Lift off

Rockets lift off every week from one of about 30 launch sites around the world. A rocket's fuel produces gas, and this is forced out of the rocket's base at high speed, propelling the rocket upwards. Its cargo, which is usually a satellite or a spacecraft – either robotic or crewed – is carried in the rocket's nose.

Man on the Moon

Nine separate *Apollo* missions carried astronauts from the US to the Moon. The fourth, *Apollo 11*, landed the first men on the lunar surface on 21 July 1969. The last three missions took Lunar Roving Vehicles. Here, Eugene Cernan – the last man on the Moon – drives across the powdery terrain.

Living in space

Today astronauts routinely live aboard the International Space Station (ISS), which is the biggest man-made craft to orbit Earth. The size of a football pitch, it travels round us about 390km (240 miles) above the ground. The station's parts were individually carried into space and constructed there. A crew of about six astronauts is usually on board.

Spacewalk

Fewer than half of all astronauts that have travelled into space have been outside their spacecraft – an activity called a spacewalk. A spacesuit gives protection and provides oxygen to breathe. Walks regularly last up to 7 hours. Throughout, the astronauts are secured to their craft.

Robotic explorers

Robotic spacecraft travel into space on our behalf. They are car- or bus-sized craft with their own power, scientific instruments, and recording and communication equipment to send their findings back to Earth. They fly by, orbit, and land on targets. *New Horizons* (right) will fly by Pluto in 2015.

One of a pair of panoramic cameras

Opportunity on Mars

The robotic craft *Opportunity* became the third rover to land on Mars when it touched down on Meridiani Planum in January 2004. It rolls across the planet at about 1cm (½in) per second, stopping now and then to investigate the Martian rock and soil using tools on its jointed arm.

Observing

Humans have been looking into space for millennia. At first they used their eyes alone, but since 1609 the telescope has let them see more and look deeper into space. Today, professional astronomers use telescopes based on Earth and in space to study the Universe. These telescopes collect light and other forms of energy.

Earth observatory

Light can travel through our planet's atmosphere and is collected by Earth-based telescopes. The most powerful are sited on mountain-tops, above the clouds, and where the air is still. Other forms of energy such as X-rays cannot make it through the atmosphere and are collected in space.

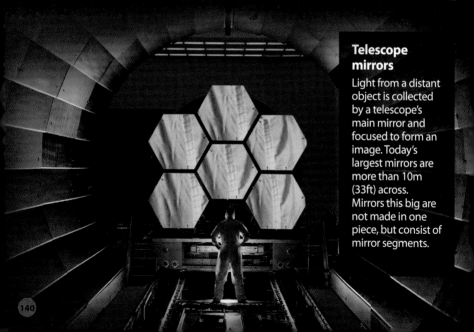

Telescope mirrors

Light from a distant object is collected by a telescope's main mirror and focused to form an image. Today's largest mirrors are more than 10m (33ft) across. Mirrors this big are not made in one piece, but consist of mirror segments.

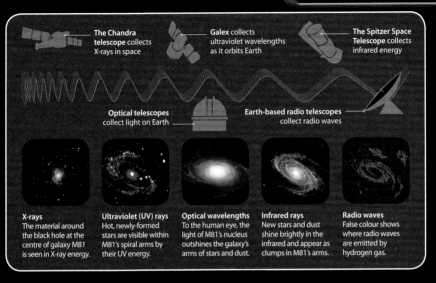

The Chandra telescope collects X-rays in space

Galex collects ultraviolet wavelengths as it orbits Earth

The Spitzer Space Telescope collects infrared energy

Optical telescopes collect light on Earth

Earth-based radio telescopes collect radio waves

X-rays
The material around the black hole at the centre of galaxy M81 is seen in X-ray energy.

Ultraviolet (UV) rays
Hot, newly-formed stars are visible within M81's spiral arms by their UV energy.

Optical wavelengths
To the human eye, the light of M81's nucleus outshines the galaxy's arms of stars and dust.

Infrared rays
New stars and dust shine brightly in the infrared and appear as clumps in M81's arms.

Radio waves
False colour shows where radio waves are emitted by hydrogen gas.

Wavelengths

Energy collected from space objects travels in wavelengths. From shorter to longer wavelengths, these include X-ray, ultraviolet, optical, infrared, and radio waves. Each reveals different aspects of an object, as can be seen in these images of galaxy M81.

Listening in

Radio waves make it to Earth's surface and are collected by huge dish telescopes. Some dishes work together and act as a giant ear listening in to space. Others listen out for signals from extraterrestrial life – none have been received yet.

Looking for yourself

Many people enjoy looking into the night sky. Using your eyes alone you can identify constellations, locate planets, and study the Moon's surface. Binoculars and telescopes reveal much more.

Answers

1 1c, 2b, 3a, 4a, 5a, 6c, 7d, 8d, 9b, 10c, 11a, 12b, 13b, 14d, 15b

2 1b, 2d, 3b, 4a, 5d, 6c, 7c, 8c, 9d, 10a, 11d, 12d, 13a, 14b, 15c, 16b, 17a, 18d, 19a, 20c

3 1d, 2a, 3a, 4b, 5c, 6a, 7b, 8d, 9b, 10b, 11b, 12c, 13c, 14a, 15c, 16d, 17d, 18d, 19c, 20a

4 1d, 2b, 3d, 4d, 5b, 6c, 7a, 8c, 9a, 10a, 11a, 12c, 13b, 14d, 15a

5 1b, 2a, 3c, 4a, 5b, 6b, 7c, 8d, 9d, 10b, 11c, 12c, 13a, 14d, 15a, 16a, 17c, 18d, 19d, 20b

6 1a, 2b, 3a, 4a, 5b, 6c, 7b, 8c, 9d, 10a, 11a, 12d, 13c, 14d, 15d, 16c, 17d, 18c, 19b, 20b

7 1b, 2b, 3d, 4b, 5d, 6a, 7c, 8d, 9b, 10a, 11c, 12c, 13c, 14a, 15a

8 1c, 2d, 3a, 4a, 5c, 6b, 7c, 8c, 9a, 10d, 11c, 12b, 13a, 14b, 15d, 16c, 17b, 18d, 19b, 20d

9 1a, 2a, 3b, 4a, 5d, 6d, 7d, 8c, 9a, 10b, 11d, 12a, 13c, 14d, 15c, 16b, 17c, 18c, 19a, 20b

10 1a, 2a, 3c, 4d, 5b, 6c, 7a, 8d, 9c, 10a, 11d, 12b, 13b, 14d, 15c

11 1b, 2d, 3c, 4a, 5a, 6c, 7b, 8a, 9a, 10d, 11c, 12b, 13d, 14c, 15c, 16b, 17d, 18c, 19b, 20d

12 1b, 2d, 3b, 4b, 5c, 6a, 7d, 8c, 9d, 10a, 11b, 12c, 13d, 14b, 15d, 16c, 17a, 18a, 19b, 20c

13 1d, 2b, 3a, 4b, 5d, 6c, 7d, 8a, 9a, 10c, 11c, 12d, 13a, 14b, 15c

14 1c, 2d, 3c, 4c, 5a, 6b, 7a, 8a, 9b, 10c, 11a, 12d, 13d, 14b, 15c, 16c, 17d, 18d, 19d, 20d

15 1a, 2b, 3d, 4a, 5b, 6b, 7d, 8d, 9a, 10c, 11c, 12c, 13a, 14d, 15a, 16c, 17d, 18a, 19c, 20b

16 1a, 2c, 3a, 4b, 5b, 6d, 7b, 8a, 9c, 10a, 11b, 12c, 13d, 14d, 15d

17 1d, 2b, 3c, 4a, 5b, 6b, 7c, 8c, 9d, 10b, 11a, 12a, 13a, 14d, 15b, 16d, 17a, 18c, 19d, 20c

18 1c, 2b, 3a, 4c, 5d, 6d, 7c, 8d, 9a, 10a, 11b, 12b, 13a, 14d, 15c, 16a, 17d, 18b, 19c, 20c

19 1a, 2b, 3b, 4c, 5d, 6b, 7a, 8d, 9b, 10c, 11a, 12c, 13c, 14a, 15d

20 1b 2c, 3a, 4a, 5a, 6a, 7b, 8d, 9a, 10d, 11c, 12d, 13b, 14c, 15d, 16b, 17b, 18c, 19c, 20d

21 1a, 2b, 3d, 4c, 5c, 6d, 7d, 8b, 9a, 10a, 11c, 12d, 13a, 14c, 15c, 16a, 17b, 18b, 19b, 20d

22 1b, 2a, 3b, 4d, 5d, 6c, 7c, 8a, 9d, 10b, 11d, 12a, 13c, 14d, 15c

23 1c, 2d, 3a, 4b, 5d, 6c, 7d, 8b, 9d, 10b, 11c, 12c, 13c, 14c, 15b, 16a, 17d, 18a, 19b, 20a

24 1a, 2a, 3d, 4b, 5d, 6b, 7d, 8a, 9a, 10c, 11d, 12d, 13c, 14b, 15c, 16d, 17d, 18c, 19c, 20b

25 1a, 2d, 3d, 4c, 5a, 6c, 7b, 8b, 9d, 10a, 11a, 12b, 13c, 14c, 15d

26 1a, 2b, 3d, 4a, 5c, 6c, 7a, 8c, 9c, 10d, 11c, 12c, 13d, 14a, 15d, 16b, 17b, 18a, 19b, 20d

27 1d, 2a, 3d, 4a, 5d, 6c, 7d, 8c, 9d, 10b, 11b, 12b, 13c, 14c, 15a, 16a, 17c, 18d, 19d, 20b

28 1a, 2d, 3a, 4b, 5d, 6b, 7b, 8a, 9b, 10c, 11d, 12d, 13a, 14c, 15c

29 1c, 2a, 3b, 4b, 5c, 6a, 7b, 8d, 9a, 10b, 11b, 12c, 13c, 14c, 15d, 16a, 17d, 18a, 19b, 20d

30 1c, 2d, 3b, 4b, 5a, 6b, 7c, 8d, 9a, 10c, 11a, 12c, 13b, 14d, 15a, 16d, 17a, 18c, 19b, 20d

31 1a, 2c, 3a, 4a, 5a, 6d, 7c, 8d, 9b, 10b, 11c, 12b, 13c, 14b, 15d

32 1c, 2c, 3a, 4a, 5d, 6d, 7c, 8c, 9a, 10b, 11c, 12d, 13a, 14d, 15b, 16d, 17b, 18a, 19b, 20b

33 1b, 2d, 3a, 4a, 5a, 6d, 7a, 8a, 9c, 10b, 11d, 12a, 13d, 14d, 15c, 16d, 17c, 18a, 19a, 20c

34 1c, 2d, 3c, 4b, 5c, 6d, 7a, 8c, 9b, 10b, 11a, 12d, 13d, 14a, 15b

35 1c, 2b, 3d, 4d, 5c, 6a, 7c, 8a, 9a, 10b, 11a, 12b, 13d, 14c, 15d, 16d, 17b, 18a, 19a, 20b

36 1d, 2a, 3a, 4d, 5b, 6c, 7a, 8c, 9b, 10b, 11d, 12d, 13a, 14d, 15b, 16d, 17c, 18c, 19d, 20c

37 1a, 2d, 3b, 4c, 5d, 6a, 7a, 8a, 9b, 10c, 11c, 12d, 13a, 14d, 15b

38 1d, 2c, 3a, 4b, 5c, 6a, 7c, 8b, 9d, 10a, 11c, 12b, 13d, 14b, 15a, 16c, 17c, 18b, 19d, 20d

39 1d, 2b, 3d, 4c, 5a, 6b, 7c, 8a, 9b, 10d, 11c, 12b, 13c, 14b, 15c, 16d, 17a, 18a, 19a, 20d

40 1d, 2d, 3b, 4d, 5d, 6c, 7b, 8a, 9c, 10c, 11a, 12b, 13a, 14c, 15a

41 1b, 2c, 3a, 4c, 5a, 6d, 7c, 8d, 9a, 10a, 11b, 12d, 13c, 14b, 15b, 16b, 17a, 18d, 19b, 20c

42 1d, 2a, 3a, 4d, 5a, 6d, 7b, 8c, 9b, 10b, 11b, 12c, 13c, 14d, 15c, 16c, 17d, 18a, 19d, 20a

43 1d, 2b, 3b, 4b, 5a, 6c, 7a, 8c, 9b, 10d, 11c, 12a, 13b, 14a, 15c

44 1c, 2d, 3b, 4a, 5d, 6a, 7a, 8c, 9c, 10c, 11d, 12b, 13b, 14c, 15a, 16d, 17d, 18a, 19a, 20b

45 1d, 2a, 3b, 4c, 5c, 6a, 7d, 8b, 9a, 10c, 11a, 12d, 13b, 14b, 15b, 16c, 17d, 18d, 19a, 20c

46 1b, 2b, 3c, 4b, 5c, 6b, 7d, 8c, 9d, 10a, 11d, 12d, 13c, 14a, 15a

47 1d, 2d, 3d, 4a, 5b, 6c, 7d, 8a, 9a, 10a, 11c, 12b, 13c, 14b, 15d, 16b, 17c, 18b, 19d, 20b

48 1a, 2c, 3c, 4b, 5a, 6a, 7a, 8c, 9d, 10b, 11b, 12b, 13d, 14b, 15b, 16d, 17c, 18c, 19c, 20a

49 1c, 2d, 3c, 4a, 5c, 6b, 7a, 8d, 9b, 10d, 11b, 12b, 13a, 14a, 15c

50 1c, 2c, 3a, 4c, 5a, 6c, 7a, 8c, 9d, 10a, 11b, 12b, 13b, 14b, 15b, 16a, 17d, 18b, 19c, 20d

51 1b, 2a, 3d, 4d, 5b, 6a, 7c, 8d, 9d, 10b, 11c, 12b, 13c, 14b, 15b, 16c, 17a, 18a, 19a, 20d

52 1a, 2b, 3d, 4a, 5c, 6b, 7c, 8c, 9d, 10a, 11b, 12a, 13b, 14d, 15d

53 1d, 2d, 3a, 4a, 5b, 6c, 7c, 8a, 9c, 10a, 11c, 12d, 13d, 14a, 15b, 16c, 17b, 18c, 19b, 20b

54 1d, 2d, 3b, 4d, 5a, 6b, 7c, 8a, 9a, 10c, 11a, 12a, 13d, 14b, 15d, 16c, 17b, 18c, 19d, 20c

55 1b, 2c, 3a, 4a, 5a, 6c, 7c, 8d, 9b, 10b, 11c, 12a, 13d, 14d, 15d

56 1a, 2c, 3b, 4d, 5d, 6a, 7a, 8c, 9a, 10c, 11c, 12d, 13d, 14b, 15d, 16b, 17b, 18d, 19a, 20c

57 1a, 2d, 3c, 4d, 5c, 6d, 7a, 8b, 9d, 10a, 11c, 12a, 13c, 14b, 15b, 16b, 17a, 18c, 19a, 20b

58 1c, 2d, 3b, 4a, 5a, 6c, 7c, 8c, 9b, 10a, 11b, 12b, 13d, 14b, 15d

59 1c, 2a, 3a, 4d, 5a, 6b, 7a, 8a, 9c, 10b, 11c, 12b, 13c, 14c, 15d, 16b, 17b, 18d, 19d, 20b

60 1d, 2c, 3b, 4a, 5c, 6c, 7d, 8d, 9b, 10a, 11d, 12c, 13c, 14b, 15d, 16a, 17b, 18a, 19d, 20b

Acknowledgments

DK would like to thank: Jenny Sich for proofreading; Sreshtha Bhattacharya, James Mitchem, and Garima Sharma for additional editorial work; and Rakesh Khundongbam and Anis Sayyed for additional design work.

The publisher would like to thank the following for their kind permission to reproduce their photographs:
(Key: a – above; b – below/bottom; c – centre; f – far; l – left; r – right; t – top)

6 NASA: Edwin E. Buzz Aldrin. **7 NASA:** NSSDC (cra). **8 NASA:** GSFC / Scientific Visualization Studio (clb, bc, bl). **9 Chandra X-Ray Observatory:** X-ray: NASA / CXC / Penn State / G. Garmire; Optical: NASA / ESA / STScI / M. West (tr). **10 Chandra X-Ray Observatory:** X-ray: NASA / CXC / U.Colorado / Linsky et al.; Optical: NASA / ESA / STScI / ASU / J.Hester & P.Scowen. (cl). **11 NASA:** The Hubble Heritage Team (AURA / STScI) / A. Fujii (cra). **13 NASA:** JPL–Caltech (br). **14 NASA:** (cl). **16 ESO:** Claus Madsen (bl). **17 NASA:** JPL–Caltech / SSC (tr). **19 NASA:** GSFC / Reto Stöckli (land surface, shallow water, clouds) Enhancements by Robert Simmon (ocean color, compositing, 3D globes, animation). Data and technical support: MODIS Land Group; MODIS Science Data Support Team; MODIS Atmosphere Group; MODIS Ocean Group Additional data: USGS EROS Data Center (topography); USGS Terrestrial Remote Sensing Flagstaff Field Center (Antarctica); Defense Meteorological Satellite Program (city lights).. **20 Corbis:** Vincent van Gogh / The Gallery Collection (tr). **21 NASA:** JPL–Caltech (br). **22 NASA:** The Hubble Heritage Team (AURA / STScI) / ESA, and the Hubble SM4 ERO Team (tl). **23 ESO:** P. Kervella, Digitized Sky Survey 2 and A. Fujii (bl). **24–25 NASA. 26 NASA:** (tr). **27 NASA:** (cla). **28 NASA:** X-ray: NASA / CXC / U.Colorado / J.Hester et al.; Optical: NASA / ESA / ASU / J.Hester & A.Loll; Infrared: NASA / JPL–Caltech / Univ. Minn. / R.Gehrz (tr). **29 NASA:** Williams College Eclipse Expedition – Jay M. Pasachoff, Muzhou Lu, and Craig Malamut (br). **30 NASA:** The Hubble Heritage Team (AURA / STScI) (b). **31 NASA:** JPL–Caltech (cra); (cr); JPL–Caltech / Alan Stern (Southwest Research Institute), Marc Buie (Lowell Observatory), NASA and ESA (c). **32 NASA:** JPL–Caltech / Univ.of Ariz. (cl). **33 NASA:** D. Roddy (tr). **34 NASA:** JPL–Caltech / Univ.of Ariz. (bl). **35 NASA:** GSFC / Scientific Visualization Studio (tl). **36 NASA:** Cassini Imaging Team, Cassini Project (bl). **37 NASA:** (l). **38 NASA:** (cl). **39 NASA:** MSFC (bl). **40 NASA:** The Hubble Heritage Team (AURA / STScI) / G. Bacon (STScI) (cl). **41 NASA:** JPL (cra). **42–43 ESO:** D. Coe (STScI) / J. Merten (Heidelberg / Bologna). **43 NASA:** (tr). **44 NASA:** JPL (cr). **45 NASA:** (tr). **48 NASA:** JPL–Caltech (tl). **49 NASA:** Neil Armstrong / Carnegie Mellon University. **50 ESO:** S. Gillessen et al (cl). **51 NASA:** (tr). **52 NASA:** (tl). **53 NASA:** AMES Research Center (bl). **54 NASA. 56 NASA:** Planetary Photojournal (cr). **57 NASA:** ESA / Herschel / PACS / SPIRE / J.Fritz, U.Gent / XMM–Newton / EPIC / W. Pietsch, MPE (cra). **58 NASA:** Kennedy Space Center (br). **59 NASA:** (tr). **60–61 NASA:** Kennedy Space Center / George Shelton. **61 NASA:** (tr). **62 NASA:** The Hubble Heritage Team (AURA / STScI) / ESA, and M. Livio (STScI) / Illustration Credit: NASA, ESA, and A. Feild (STScI). **63 NASA:** JPL / Space Science Institute (tl). **64 Courtesy of U.S. Army:** Navy Petty Officer 1st Class Matthew Bradley (cl). **66 NASA:** (cl). **66–67 NASA:** JPL / STScI. **68 NASA:** JPL–Caltech / UCLA (tr). **69 NASA:** USGS / EROS Data Center (bl). **70 NASA:** (fclb, bl, clb, bl). **71 NASA:** JPL (tr). **73 NASA:** JPL (cr). **74 NASA:** (bl). **75 NASA:** (tr). **76 NASA:** ESA, H. Bond (STScI) and M. Barstow (University of Leicester) (tl). **77 NASA:** JPL. **78 NASA:** Mir–Crew. **80 NASA:** JPL–Caltech / UCLA (bl). **81 NASA:** CXC / ASU / J. Hester et al (tr). **82 NASA:** GSFC (bl). **83 NASA:** (cr). **84 NASA:** (tr). **86 NASA:** JPL (bl). **87 NASA:** SOHO Consortium, EIT, ESA (tl). **88 NASA:** (tr). **89 NASA:** ESA, M. Robberto (Space Telescope Science Institute / ESA) and the Hubble Space Telescope Orion Treasury Project Team (tr). **90 Corbis:** Tony Hallas / Science Faction. **92 NASA:** ESA, J. Hester, A. Loll (ASU) (br). **93 NASA:** (cl). **94 NASA:** JPL / Ted Stryk (bl). **95 NASA:** STS–116 Shuttle Crew (tr). **96 NASA. 97 NASA:** Damian Peach, Amateur Astonomer (tr). **99 NASA:** GSFC / The Royal Swedish Academy of Sciences (tr). **101 NASA:** (cl). **102 ESO:** J. Linder (bl). **105 NASA:** Cassini Imaging Team, SSI, JPL, ESA (cr). **106 NASA:** JPL (cl). **107 NASA:** Johns Hopkins University Applied Physics Laboratory / Arizona State University / Carnegie Institution of Washington. Image reproduced courtesy of Science / AAAS (tr). **109 NASA. 110 NASA:** TIROS Program (cl). **111 NASA:** JPL / Texas A&M / Cornell (tr). **112 NASA:** Johns Hopkins University Applied Physics Laboratory / Carnegie Institution of Washington (br). **113 ESO:** (bl). **114 NASA:** JPL / USGS (bl). **114–115 NASA:** JPL / Space Science Institute. **116 NASA:** (tr). **117 NASA:** ESA (tl). **118 NASA:** JPL–Caltech / Harvard–Smithsonian (tr). **119 NASA:** (cr). **120 NASA. 122 NASA:** (br). **124 NASA:** Russell Croman (br). **125 NASA:** CalTech (cl). **126 NASA:** ESA / S. Beckwith (STScI) and The HUDF Team (clb); WMAP Science Team (br). **126–127 NASA:** The Hubble Heritage Team (AURA / STScI) / NOAO / AURA / NSF, B. Twardy, B. Twardy, and A. Block (NOAO) (t). **127 ESO:** G. Hüdepohl (b). **Science Photo Library:** Robert Gendler (cr). **128 ESO:** J. Emerson / VISTA (bl). **NASA:** ESA, H. Bond (STScI) and M. Barstow (University of Leicester) (cl); JPL–Caltech (cr). **129 NASA:** The Hubble Heritage Team (AURA / STScI) / ESA and AURA / Caltech (cl); JPL–Caltech (cr). **131 Dorling Kindersley:** The Royal Ontario Museum, Toronto (tl). **NASA:** ESA / SOHO (bl); GSFC / The Royal Swedish Academy of Sciences (crb). **132 NASA:** GSFC / Reto Stöckli (land surface, shallow water, clouds). Enhancements by Robert Simmon (ocean color, compositing, 3D globes, animation). Data and technical support: MODIS Land Group; MODIS Science Data Support Team; MODIS Atmosphere Group; MODIS Ocean Group Additional data: USGS EROS Data Center (topography); USGS Terrestrial Remote Sensing Flagstaff Field Center (Antarctica); Defense Meteorological Satellite Program (city lights). (cr); JPL / Mosaic by Mattias Malmer (ca); Johns Hopkins University Applied Physics Laboratory / Smithsonian Institution / Carnegie Institution of Washington (br). **133 NASA:** JPL (t); JPL–Caltech / Cornell / NMMNH (cl); (br). **134–135 NASA:** JPL / Space Science Institute. **134 NASA:** The Hubble Heritage Team (AURA / STScI) / M. Wong and I. de Pater (University of California, Berkeley) (bl). **135 NASA:** JPL / Space Science Institute (tr); Erich Karkoschka, University of Arizona (cla); JPL / Galileo Project (bl). **136 NASA:** JPL / USGS (r). **136–137 NASA:** (t). **137 ESO:** (tr). **NASA:** (bl); Katsuhiro Mouri & Shuji Kobayashi (Nagoya City Science Museum / Planetarium) (crb). **138 NASA:** (cl, r). **139 NASA:** (tr, cla, crb). **140 ESO:** (cr). **NASA:** MSFC / David Higginbotham (b). **141 NASA:** CXC / Wisconsin / D. Pooley & CfA / A. Zezas (fcla); (cla, fcra); ESA and the Hubble Heritage Team (STScI / AURA) / A. Zezas and J. Huchra (Harvard–Smithsonian Center for Astrophysics) (ca); JPL–Caltech (cra). **Science Photo Library:** David Nunuk (crb).

Jacket images: Front: Dreamstime.com: Vangelis Liolios (mars). NASA: JPL–Caltech bl.

All other images © Dorling Kindersley
For further information see: www.dkimages.com